Building a Teen Center

An Integrated
Algebra Project

Mary Ann Christina

D1510891

KEY CURRICULUM PRESS
Innovators in Mathematics Education

Editor Sarah E. Block

Editorial Contributors Masha Albrecht and James A. Browne

Editorial Assistant James A. Browne

Reviewers John Chart and Gwen Hogin

Production Editor Caroline Ayres

Copyeditor Margaret Moore

Interior Design Kirk Mills

Layout Ann Rothenbuhler

Illustration Nathan Stephens

Technical Illustration Ben Turner Graphics

Cover Design Maryann Ohki

Design Coordinator Diana Krevsky

Prepress DMI

Publisher Steven Rasmussen

Editorial Director John Bergez

Key Curriculum Press
P.O. Box 2304
Berkeley, CA 94702
510-548-2304
editorial@keypress.com
http://www.keypress.com

Printed in the United States of America   10 9 8 7 6 5 4 3 2 1   02 01 00 99 98   ISBN 1-55953-310-2

About the Author

Mary Ann Christina is currently Gifted Education Mathematics Coordinator for Broward County Schools in Florida. Formerly she was the mathematics department chairperson at Coral Springs High School in Coral Springs, Florida, and the mathematics depart-ment chairperson at Deerfield Beach High School in Broward County, Florida. She has taught Algebra I and Algebra II for 14 years in Florida and for 9 years in upstate New York. She has been very involved in the Florida Opening the Gate philosophy—"Algebra for All"—and has spoken at Florida Council of Mathematics Teachers' Conferences.

Mary Ann Christina is the recipient of the 1990 Deerfield Beach High School Teacher of the Year award, and the 1992 Broward County High School Teacher of the Year award. She is also the 1996 Presidential Awardee in Secondary Mathematics for the State of Florida.

In her limited free time she can be found on the golf course in pursuit of negative numbers, which unfortunately do not happen very often.

Contents

Preface   vii

Overview   1

Unit 1: A Dream of a Teen Center   7

Unit 2: The Blueprint   17

    Lesson 2-1: Measurement, Area, and Perimeter   19

    Lesson 2-2: Creating a Beautiful Classroom   24

    Lesson 2-3: Finding the Area of Irregular Figures   28

    Lesson 2-4: Scale Drawings   33

    Lesson 2-5: Drawing the Blueprint   38

    Lesson 2-6: Blueprint Written Report   45

Unit 3: Designing the Rooms   49

    Lesson 3-1: Three-Dimensional Coordinates   51

    Lesson 3-2: Volume and Surface Area   58

    Lesson 3-3: Linear/Quadratic Equations
             Based on Area (Optional)   64

    Lesson 3-4: Introduction to Matrices   70

    Lesson 3-5: Multiplication of Matrices   78

    Lesson 3-6: Design and Costs of Rooms Report   86

Unit 4: Projected Expenses per Month   91

    Lesson 4-1: Spreadsheets, Pie Charts, and Bar Graphs   93

    Lesson 4-2: Projected Expenses for the Teen Center   99

Unit 5: Making a Profit   105

    Lesson 5-1: The Cartesian Coordinate System   107

    Lesson 5-2: Developing an Equation   111

    Lesson 5-3: Slope and y-Intercept   114

    Lesson 5-4: Designing the Logo and Menu   121

    Lesson 5-5: Making a Profit   124

Unit 6: Building the Physical Model   131

    Lesson 6-1: Building the Model   134

Unit 7: The Business Loan   139

    Lesson 7-1: Paper-Folding Problem   141

    Lesson 7-2: Allowance Problem   145

    Lesson 7-3: Savings Account Problem   150

    Lesson 7-4: Home Mortgage Problem   154

    Lesson 7-5: Teen Center Business Loan   159

Unit 8: Analysis of Teen Center Project   161

Answers to Selected Exercises   165

Appendix: Graphing Calculator Notes   173

Preface

Finally, modeling authentic problems permits and encourages a diversity of approaches thereby promoting greater access by a broader population to meaningful mathematics.

—NCTM, *Algebra in a Technological World*, 1995

On a Monday night in January, my algebra class went to a meeting of the Deerfield Beach Florida City Commission to demonstrate a project that they had created. That night was a very special evening as the mayor presented us to the commission and the audience. There was a piece of property that the city could not decide how to develop. My class had applied their mathematical skills and, working in project teams, developed proposals for building a teen center as a possible use for the land. The students took the presentations quite seriously; and after they finished, they received an ovation. It was a very precious and wonderful moment.

This book is an outgrowth of this experience. *Building a Teen Center* is an integrated algebra project in which students directly apply the mathematics they are learning. Students work in project teams to design and develop a teen center. As one of the assistant administrators at my school said, "It is a pleasure indeed to see 'problem' students bring their projects to their administrators' offices and remind them to come up and see their final presentations. Students are experiencing success and want to be caught 'doing good.'"

As educational standards in the country move toward a mandated algebra course for all high school graduates, we must distinguish "traditional" algebra, which only manipulates variables and constants, from a way of thinking mathematically that uses equations to analyze important relationships and allows us to make predictions about future behavior. Since the 1980s, the National Council of Teachers of Mathematics has called for decreased emphasis on manipulative algebra, where so much time is spent simplifying radicals and rational expressions and factoring polynomials. Instead, the NCTM has asked us, as mathematics teachers, to concentrate on

- actively involving students in applying mathematical ideas,
- using problem solving as a means and a goal of instruction,
- using a variety of instructional formats that include small cooperative groups, individualized exploration, projects, and whole class instruction and discussion, and
- using calculators and computers as tools for learning mathematics.

One way to achieve these goals is to integrate real problems and situations into the curriculum. *Building a Teen Center* does that and promotes meaningful mathematics through application. As students draw designs and blueprints, build their physical models, project their profits and expenses, and procure business loans, they use a lot of algebra. Moreover, students retain and value the mathematics they use in this project. As one of my students stated in a newspaper article: "Before [the project], I [thought] 'Why do I need to know linear equations?' . . . We found out why. . . . I will never forget how to use these concepts now."

Because the teen center project cannot be completed in a day or even a week, I recommend using it throughout the entire school year. As a teacher, you may feel that you do not have the time to take from your curriculum to do a project of this magnitude, but it is important for students to see a relationship between the concepts they are learning and how they might use them in their future work or personal world. This is a unique challenge when working with a diverse group of students. In the class where I piloted the project, at least half of the students came from Haiti, many students' families did not speak English, and most of the students in the class came from families that lived at or below the poverty line. My goal was to heighten their motivation for school and improve their ability to learn and retain important mathematics. By doing the project, my students developed a different appreciation of and respect for the use of mathematics.

My goal in teaching algebra is not to create a student who is merely computationally efficient, but rather a student who can think algebraically and understand algebraic ideas in order to solve complex problems. Our students face an uncertain and dynamic world. It is imperative that they become thoughtful, open-minded, and productive individuals who can cope with complex situations and are prepared to offer different types of solutions in an ever-changing, technological society.

Acknowledgments

I have so many people to thank for this experience. I would like to thank Larry Wantuck and Gerry Greer (my former mathematics supervisors), Anne Lynch (assistant principal), John Meyer (guidance director), and Ronald Clodfelter (principal) for supporting me with this project in the classroom and then encouraging me to have it published.

Thank you to Bonnie Blohm, Marian Anderson, Hallie Hopper, and Connie Oshry for using the project in their classrooms and believing in the philosophy wholeheartedly. Also, a very special thank you to Connie and Hallie for being such special and great friends.

A big thank you to a great editor, Sarah Block, for a lot of patience, guidance, and understanding with a first-time writer.

It was because of Bob Davis's great activities that the teen center project started. Without his inspiration and encouragement, this book would not have been written. Thank you so much.

Mary Ann Christina

Building a Teen Center

An Integrated Algebra Project

The purpose of *Building a Teen Center* is to supplement, not replace, your current Algebra I or Integrated Math I and II curriculum. This project allows students an opportunity to practice and apply skills that they should have attained already in your classroom. The project is most effective if it is undertaken from start to finish. However, if you do not wish to do the entire project, many of the activities in this book can be used separately to enhance your own curriculum.

The Units

This book is divided into eight units. Each unit begins with a brief description of the entire unit, a list of the **mathematical concepts** that are explored and the **lessons** that develop the mathematical concepts, plus some **assessment** suggestions. In each unit, students develop a different set of mathematical skills necessary to work on the project. For example, in Unit 5: Making a Profit, in order to write a business plan, students review graphing linear equations, interpreting slope, and reading a graph. In the last lesson of each unit, students work on the teen center. If you do not have time for all the material, the review activities may be done independently from the project. If you do not have time for the entire project, you might choose to do some parts of the teen center, such as the blueprint, room design, and model, or the business plan and loan application.

Unit 1: A Dream of a Teen Center

This unit introduces and sets the foundation for the project. Students are organized into groups (suggestions on how to group the students are in the unit), devise a name for their teen center, make a preliminary sketch, assign job responsibilities, and determine the purpose of the project. This unit should take one or two days and is a prerequisite for the entire book.

Unit 2: The Blueprint

In this unit, each group draws the blueprint for their teen center. The mathematical concepts used in this unit include measurement, use of formulas, ratio and proportion, area and perimeter, distance formula, and the Pythagorean theorem.

Prerequisite: Unit 1

Unit 3: Designing the Rooms

Students design and calculate the costs of each of the rooms in their teen center. The mathematical concepts developed in this unit include volume, coordinates in three-dimensions, matrices, and linear and quadratic equations.

Prerequisites: Units 1 and 2

Unit 4: Projected Expenses per Month

Students calculate their projected expenses per month and create and interpret statistical data. They develop pie charts and bar graphs both by hand and by computer. This unit offers a wonderful opportunity to introduce spreadsheet applications on computers.

Prerequisite: Unit 1

Unit 5: Making a Profit

Each group has the opportunity to find ways to make a profit with their teen center. The mathematical concepts used in this unit include slope, domain and range, realistic interpretation of graphs, mathematical limitations of equations, and the development of a linear function. Added features include learning to use a graphing calculator and appreciating its capabilities, designing a logo, creating T-shirts to advertise their teen center, and designing a menu using a computer.

Prerequisites: Units 1 and 4

Unit 6: Building the Physical Model

This unit is always the most exciting for me and my students because this is when they build their physical models. My students loved focusing on the details of building model tables, couches, pool tables, and dance floors. They actually have the opportunity to turn two dimensions into three dimensions. If nothing else, during this part of the project, I learned that when one has a purpose, working is no longer a problem. Students, as well as anyone, have self-discipline when they have a reason to be engaged.

Prerequisites: Units 1, 2, and 3

Unit 7: The Business Loan

This unit focuses on exponential functions, beginning with paper folding and culminating with complicated formulas used by financial institutions to calculate mortgages. A loan officer's visit to the classroom enhances the unit. In order to build their teen center, the students must apply for a business loan, and it is important for them to understand how that is done.

Prerequisites: Units 1, 4, and 5

Unit 8: Analysis of Teen Center Project

At the conclusion of the project, each student will analyze the project by describing his or her role (leader or follower), and assess satisfaction or dissatisfaction with that role and team members' roles. Students will also describe what they learned mathematically, the aspect of the project they enjoyed most and why, and the greatest problem their group encountered and how they solved it.

Lesson Plans

Each unit is divided into one or more lessons. Each lesson plan includes the following information:

- a brief **overview**
- an **objective** or **objectives**
- a list of the **materials** needed
- a list of necessary **resources** including transparencies

Each lesson plan is not based strictly around a single day; it may take a series of days to complete a lesson. Estimates of time periods are provided, but based on the skill level of your class, some lessons may take more or less time to complete. The lesson plans are based on a sequence that follows the progression of the project, not necessarily on a "normal" sequence provided in an Algebra I text. However, the sequence is logical in that students are exposed to such concepts as measurement, area, surface area, volume, linear and quadratic equations, matrices, statistics, development of linear equations, and exponential equations in that order. Both the graphing calculator and computer have been incorporated into the lessons, but if these are not available to you, the lessons can be done without them.

Each lesson has one or more of the following activities: a **class activity**, **group activity**, **partner activity**, **individual activity**, or **home activity**.

 Class Activity

The class activity opens the lesson and provides instructional time to introduce and explain what mathematical concepts the lesson will cover. The class activity is not based on a lecture, but rather on whole class instruction, whereby you and the students work through a manipulative activity. Also, the class activity provides time to review the home assignment from the night before.

Group Activity

Michael Serra states in *Discovering Geometry Teacher's Guide and Answer Key:* "It struck me as ironic that we stress competition and working independently in our schools, while business and industry stress cooperation, not competition, in problem solving." In just about every lesson, you will find group activities that demand the students work together and not independently. The activities included in this book promote group interaction and collaborative problem solving.

If you have not used **cooperative learning** before, some of the group activities can help orient you to a different but constructive way for students to learn by doing. Instead of teaching with the entire class as your audience, break down the class into groups of four. As the teacher, recognize their performance as a group, instead of as individuals. Other types of activities will enable you to evaluate them as individuals. The biggest shock that you will encounter the first time you use cooperative learning is noise. The idea is to keep that noise constructive and to get group members to work and talk without yelling at each other. As you walk around the room observing, you can work with any groups that have difficulty grasping this concept. Also, it is imperative that you have some type of signal (for example, raising your hand, or putting your hands on top of your head) to bring the class back to order so that you can talk to them.

 Partner Activity

There are a few activities in the book that require two or three people to complete. These are simply called partner activities. Sometimes when students learn new material they can be overwhelmed working alone; and if they are not strong students they can get lost in a group of four. This type of activity provides them an opportunity to bounce ideas off another person without feeling intimidated or embarrassed about not knowing a concept in a larger group.

 Individual Activity

There are two ways I use an individual activity: as a source of individual assessment and as a way to determine if students understand the material and are on the right track. These activities provide them an opportunity to work alone without collaboration from their peers.

Home Activity

The home activities are designed to reinforce the material covered in class. The day following their assignment, you might have students review their home assignments within their group or make oral presentations to the class, or you could collect them to evaluate the students' progress. Some of the home activities are designed as assessment activities unique to their own situation. For example, Home Activity 2-5: Home Floor Plan is based on the student doing a floor plan of her or his own home or apartment.

A Dream of a Teen Center

The Curriculum and Evaluation Standards paints mathematics as an activity and a process, not simply as a body of content to be mastered. Throughout, there is an emphasis on doing mathematics, recognizing connections, and valuing the enterprise.

—NCTM, *Algebra in a Technological World*, 1995

In Unit 1, introduce your students to the entire project and provide them with the basic organizational structure to work on the project. Unit 1 is designed to be done in one day. However, for shorter class periods (about 45 minutes), it may take one and a half days. After the students complete Unit 1, I suggest proceeding directly to Unit 2 for cohesiveness.

Objectives

- Introduce the project
- Assign groups
- Give an overview of the parts of the project
- Have students name their teen center
- Have students choose project roles
- Introduce and set up the daily journal
- Have students make a preliminary sketch
- Have students fill out the preliminary information sheet

Materials

- Deck of cards (ace through 8 or 9—optional)
- One notebook or binder per group (you may choose to purchase these in advance for your students)
- Several sheets of drawing paper per group

Resources

- Transparency 1-1: Request for Teen Center Proposals
- Project Schedule
- Group Activity 1-1: Getting Started
- Individual Activity 1-1: Daily Journal (ten daily journal sheets per student)
- Home Activity 1-1: Preliminary Information Sheet

Introducing the Project

In the preface, I mentioned that my students presented their completed projects at a city commission meeting and were praised by all concerned. As their consulting firm and teacher, I took great joy in their success and pride in their accomplishments. This project will give you an opportunity to bring the integration of algebra and geometry to life in the building of a teen center.

When introducing the project to my own students, I explained to them that there was a mathematical purpose to the project and that they would have an opportunity to use their algebra and geometry by creating and doing a project that typifies a real-world setting. My students were very excited about the prospect of putting algebra and geometry to use. There had been too many times when my students would ask, "When are we ever going to use this?" This project gave them an answer that they could relate to.

Deerfield Beach High School where I piloted the project is located in a low-income area and most of my students were Haitian, Latino, or African American. My students had high aspirations and most were planning to continue their education after high school. To help them achieve their goals, I continually tried to inspire and motivate them, so I added a nonmathematical purpose to the project. The juvenile crime rate was high in the area, so I included the following statement to appeal to their needs as teenagers.

> The City Commission of Deerfield Beach, Florida, has asked the Christina Consulting Firm to come up with possible proposals and plans for a Teen Center to alleviate the problem of too many teenagers on the streets with nothing to do in the evenings. The City Commission feels that if students had an alternative social outlet, some of the crime and destruction of property that is taking place in evening hours might be alleviated.

You can fill in **Transparency 1-1: Request for Teen Center Proposals** to introduce the project, or you may want to customize the nonmathematical purpose of the project to best suit the needs and interests of the students in your classroom and area.

Assigning Groups

For this project, it is nice to have groups of four. There are several different and effective ways to form groups. If you have been using cooperative learning regularly in your classroom, then use what works for you and your classes. However, if you are a novice and are looking for some helpful hints, here are two different methods.

Random Selection

- Have a computer randomly select different groups (certain grade-book programs have this feature)
- When students walk in the door, give them a playing card from the ace through the 8 (i.e., for 32 students).
- Use a spinner or colored index cards.

Ability Levels

- Create groups of four such that there is one high, two medium, and one low achiever per group.

I discovered that it was not a good idea to let students choose their own groups. There are always students who do not get chosen, and there are groups who just want to socialize and lose their entire purpose when they get together. Also, there are always students who do not like to attend classes. I might let those students work together if there are enough of them.

Introducing the Parts of the Project

When introducing the project to students, it is important to list the various parts of the project and give a brief explanation of what those parts will entail, including a description of the mathematics involved. At this time, each group should receive the **Project Schedule**, which provides an overview of the entire project. In addition, it is useful to provide each group with a small notebook or binder in which to keep their daily journals, reports, pictures, and a completion record.

After going over the parts of the project, direct each group to come up with a name for their teen center. This may take more time than you might expect.

Assignment of Jobs

Give **Group Activity 1-1: Getting Organized** to each group so that students can write down the name of their teen center and who has what jobs. They can choose from *project leader, recorder, statistician,* and *engineer*. Remind them that all group members should participate in all parts of the project. However, each member of the group has a position in the company that makes him or her responsible for certain facets of the final presentation for each part. Give each group the criteria for each position and then have them choose the position that best suits them. Students should keep the completed Getting Started sheet in their notebook.

Preliminary Sketch

Now that the students have an understanding of what the project is about, let each group make a preliminary sketch of what they would like their teen center to look like, such as rooms, layout of tables, games, dance floor, and so on. Let their creative juices flow. Have them sketch their plan on an $8\frac{1}{2}$-by-11-inch unlined sheet of paper. On another sheet, have them write down the items (furniture, tables, jukeboxes, and so on) that they think would be necessary in their teen center. If my students thought it could happen, I never discouraged their dream. Reality comes soon enough and many of my students had to discard parts of their original dream. After the students have completed their preliminary sketches and dream items, they should put them in their notebooks.

Daily Journal

The purpose of the Daily Journal is to help students organize their work and their time and stay on task. It also allows you, as the teacher, to determine how smoothly things are working within the group and to notice the various problems they may be having. Students should take a few minutes at the end of each class to fill out a Daily Journal. (A black line master of the daily journal pages appears in Unit 1 and can be photocopied for this purpose.)

Home Activity 1-1
Preliminary Information Sheet

This activity asks students to obtain preliminary information on costs and formulas that will be needed to build their teen centers. Each group should complete the assignment before they start their blueprint. If you assign different groups to get different information, there will not be multiple calls to the same organization and then each group can complete the sheet by combining all of the groups' efforts.

Request for Teen Center Proposals

To: _____ Classes

From: The _____ Consulting Firm

Re: Building a Teen Center in _____

The City Commission of _____ has asked the _____ Consulting Firm to come up with possible proposals and plans for a Teen Center. The purpose of this Teen Center is_____

_____

_____

_____

_____

Therefore, the _____ Consulting Firm is contacting _____ classes at _____ High School to develop viable proposals for the construction of such a Teen Center. The best proposals will be presented to the City Commission upon completion of the project.

The _____ Consulting Firm hopes to have several acceptable proposals and physical models to present to the City Commission and hopes all teams are concerned citizens and will put forth their best effort!

Name _____

Project Schedule

Description	Date due	Date completed
Unit 1: A Dream of a Teen Center Create a preliminary drawing and written description of the teen center.		
Unit 2: The Blueprint Complete a scale drawing of the teen center and write a report.		
Unit 3: Designing the Rooms Design rooms and calculate construction cost for interior and exterior portions of the building. Write a report.		
Unit 4: Projected Expenses per Month Create a spreadsheet to project monthly costs of operating the center.		
Unit 5: Making a Profit Create a menu and business logo for the center. Make calculations to determine how to make the business profitable.		
Unit 6: Building the Physical Model Build a scale model of the teen center.		
Unit 7: The Business Loan Present your business plan to a loan officer and secure a loan to start your business.		
Unit 8: Analysis of Teen Center Project Write a report analyzing your role and accomplishments in the project.		

Getting Started

Your team goal is to assign one of the following executive jobs to each member.

Available Executive Jobs

Project leader: The project leader is responsible for taking daily attendance, keeping the daily journal, overseeing all work, making decisions when controversies occur, and making final decisions on completed work and presentations. The project leader is also responsible for meeting deadlines and making sure the entire team is on task.

Recorder: The recorder writes down ideas, makes phone calls, coordinates all paper work, and types all final reports.

Statistician: The statistician gets the necessary equipment for the day, applies formulas, creates equations, and draws the final graphs and diagrams.

Engineer: The engineer is responsible for coming up with the final ideas for construction of diagrams, buildings, and development of applicable formulas, equations, and measurements. The engineer will also be responsible for constructing the final physical model.

Getting Started

Project Leader _____ **Recorder**_____

Statistician _____ **Engineer** _____

Teen Center Name

After assigning the project roles, your group needs to decide on a name for your center.

Teen Center Name _____

Preliminary Sketch

On an $8\frac{1}{2}$-by-11-inch unlined sheet of paper, make a preliminary sketch of what your group would like your teen center to look like. Include rooms, layout of tables, games, dance floor, and so on. On another sheet of paper, write a list of ideas for your center.

Name _____

Daily Journal

Teen Center Name _____ Date _____

Role _____

Task(s) to be completed today:

Problems encountered:

Resolutions to problems:

Task(s) actually completed today:

Daily Journal

Teen Center Name _____ Date _____

Role _____

Task(s) to be completed today:

Problems encountered:

Resolutions to problems:

Task(s) actually completed today:

Preliminary Information Sheet

Your group needs to contact the following organizations and companies to get preliminary information on costs and formulas that will be necessary to complete your teen center. When you call, emphasize the fact that you need this information for a school project. Be polite and courteous and thank the people you talk to. It is important that you tell them that *the square footage involved is 9000 square feet and that your building is for entertainment.*

Maximum capacity formula (fire department): _____

_____

Approximate construction costs per square foot (construction firm):

_____

Approximate electricity costs per month (power and light company):

_____

Approximate water costs per month (water company): _____

_____

Minimal square footage for a kitchen and restrooms (zoning commission):

_____

Minimal degree of steepness for a handicapped ramp (architect or zoning

commission): _____

The Blueprint

Geometry enables the investigator to explore the formation of shapes to describe them in terms of dimension and scaling.

—NCTM, *A Core Curriculum*, 1992

In Unit 1, each group had the opportunity to dream and record group members' ideas about what they want in their teen center. Now, each group will implement and vitalize those ideas with the drawing of their blueprint.

By creating their own blueprint for their teen center, each group will have the opportunity to build on their conceptual understanding, engage in meaningful activity, and use their creativity and problem-solving skills. You will see a very productive and excited group of students.

In this unit, there are four lessons of preparation before students actually begin the teen center blueprint. If you feel your class does not need to review the concepts in these lessons, then you could begin with Lesson 2-5: Drawing the Blueprint. However, the review lessons will lead to far fewer questions and better blueprints. In the first four lessons, the groups are applying what they know, not simply repeating work they have done in the past.

If students have had little experience with cooperative learning, the first four lessons will give them the opportunity to get to know and work with each other prior to starting a major project.

Mathematical Concepts

- Measurement
- Area and perimeter
- Ratio and proportion
- Scale drawings
- Pythagorean theorem
- Distance formula

Lessons

- 2-1: Measurement, Area, and Perimeter
- 2-2: Creating a Beautiful Classroom
- 2-3: Finding the Area of Irregular Figures
- 2-4: Scale Drawings
- 2-5: Drawing the Blueprint
- 2-6: Blueprint Written Report

Assessment

There is no traditional individual assessment, such as a quiz or a test. However, Home Activity 2-2: Cost Proposal to Parents and Home Activity 2-5: Home Floor Plan are excellent assessment activities. Other forms of authentic assessment applicable to when students are working in their groups are teacher observation and peer assessment.

Measurement, Area, and Perimeter

In Unit 1, the students formed groups and dreamed about how they want their teen centers to look. It is now time to explain to them that they have to master and review measurement in order to develop an accurate and feasible blueprint. Measurement is a pre-algebra topic, but it warrants a review because some students may never have applied their knowledge about area and perimeter before. This lesson exposes the students to different types of geometric figures.

Objective

- To help students develop the ability to measure quantities in the real world and use those measurements to solve problems

Materials

- Rulers
- Calculators
- Compasses
- Graph paper $\left(\frac{1}{4} \text{ inch}\right)$

Resources

- Transparency 2-1: Area and Perimeter
- Individual Activity 2-1: Reviewing Area and Perimeter
- Home Activity 2-1: Working with Area and Perimeter

 Class Activity 2-1
Area and Perimeter   20 minutes

Because students may want to use different types of designs in their teen centers, it is important to review area and perimeter formulas for different geometric figures.

Ask the students to take a piece of notebook paper (rectangle) and measure its length and width, then find the perimeter and area of the paper. This provides an opportunity to discuss the differences between area and perimeter and to talk about dimensions.

Have the students take a piece of grid paper or $\frac{1}{4}$-inch graph paper and draw a right triangle with a base of 6 units and a height of 4 units. Discuss finding the area and perimeter of the triangle.

Note: You might also draw an acute and an obtuse triangle and ask students to find the area and perimeter.

Then ask the students to draw a circle with a 2-inch radius on their paper and find the circumference and area of the circle.

Depending on your students' backgrounds, you might also include parallelograms, trapezoids, rhombuses, and so on. Ask the groups if they have any unusual designs in mind. In this way, problems in finding the area of those designs could be addressed now.

Individual Activity 2-1
Reviewing Area and Perimeter   20 minutes

This opening worksheet gives students an opportunity to review their skills. Let them work in their teen center groups, which will give you an opportunity to observe them working in a cooperative learning situation. Problem 10 may be worth observing.

Home Activity 2-1
Working with Area and Perimeter   20 minutes

Because this is the first homework assignment, it is a good time to explain that you expect homework to be completed. If students are having difficulty with the assignment, suggest that they call one of their teen center group members. If they are still having difficulty, ask them to write everything they can do with the problem and prepare pertinent questions to ask in class the next day.

Area and Perimeter

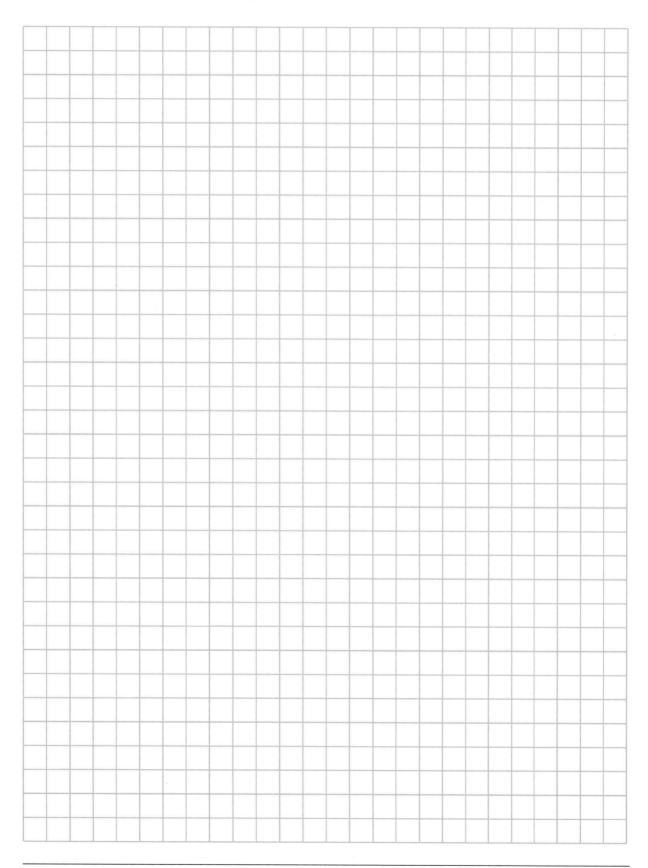

Reviewing Area and Perimeter

On a separate sheet of paper answer the questions below.

1. Take your ruler and measure the length and width of your desk (in inches).

2. What is the perimeter of your desk in inches? in feet?

3. What is the area of your desk in square inches? in square feet?

4. Draw a circle on your paper that has a radius of 1 inch.

5. What is the circumference of your circle?

6. What is the area of your circle?

7. a. Draw a right triangle on your paper that has a base of 3 inches and a height of 2 inches.
   b. What is the perimeter of your triangle?
   c. What is the area of your triangle?

8. It is said that from the tip of one's thumb to the joint in the middle of the thumb is the "human inch." How close is your inch to an actual inch?

9. Find the length of the picture at right to the nearest quarter of an inch.

10. Make an accurate drawing of 1 square inch and shade $\frac{1}{4}$ square inch.

11. Draw a vertical line segment 1.5 inches in length.

12. Draw a horizontal line segment 5.25 inches in length.

Building a Teen Center
©1998 Key Curriculum Press

Working with Area and Perimeter

On a separate sheet of paper answer the questions below.

1. A rectangle has a perimeter of 34 feet and an area of 60 square feet. What are its dimensions?

2. A rectangle has a perimeter of 32 meters and an area of 60 square meters. What are its dimensions?

3. Use the diagram below.

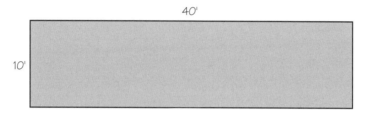

a. What is the area of the rectangle?
b. Sketch four distinct rectangles that have the same area.
c. Find the perimeter of the original rectangle and the perimeters of the rectangles you created. Are the perimeters the same?

4. Find the area of the unshaded region.

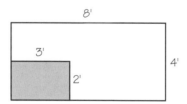

5. Use the diagram below.
a. Find the area of the shaded region.

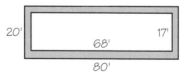

b. The unshaded region is the amount of usable space on each floor of an office building. If a company rents three full floors, how much space will the company be *unable* to use?

Creating a Beautiful Classroom

This lesson helps give students a sense of physical space. Before starting
Group Activity 2-2, my students gave estimates of what they thought the
dimensions of our classroom were. Some of their answers were astounding.

Objective
- To continue to help students develop the ability to measure quantities
  in the real world and use those measurements to solve problems

Materials
- Yardsticks
- Calculators
- Rulers

Resources
- Group Activity 2-2: Creating a Beautiful Classroom
- Home Activity 2-2: Cost Proposal

Class Activity
Class Discussion on Home Activity 2-1   10 minutes

When students enter class each day, have them sit in their teen center
groups and discuss their answers to the homework problems within their
group. Ask different groups to present their answers. As they are discussing
their answers, you might circulate to see who has completed their
homework and who has not. This is a good time to explain the importance
of doing the homework assignments in order to be successful with their
teen centers. You can put Problem 3 on the board to see if all the possible
rectangles were found. Also, Problem 5b is a good discussion problem. It
helps students become aware of what is usable space and what might be
unusable space in their teen centers.

Group Activity 2-2
Creating a Beautiful Classroom   45 minutes

Pass out Group Activity 2-2 and have students read through it for any
preliminary questions. Before they start their measurements, ask them what
they think the dimensions of the floor, walls, windows, or doors are. Put the
various estimates on the board and see who or what group was the closest
after the measurements are made.

You can also discuss how many square inches are in a square foot and how many square feet are in a square yard. This information is important when they answer the questions on painting and carpeting.

They should start in different areas of the room so that all groups are not measuring the same areas at the same time. You can also use an office, a gymnasium, or other areas to avoid congestion in the classroom.

Circulate among the groups to make sure they are using inches and feet and not centimeters and meters. If you have tape measures, use them because their measurements will be more accurate than those made with a yardstick. The physical education department might be able to provide you with tape measures.

If your cooperative learning activities have been minimal in the past, be prepared for excitement and noise in your classroom. However, I think you will find it to be constructive noise.

If students become confused with the carpeting and the painting questions, offer helpful hints, but try to get them to do as much on their own as possible. Their ability to read and follow instructions is important.

At the conclusion of the activity, have different groups present the activity orally. This is an excellent opportunity to communicate what they have learned in the activity. Also, offer the opportunity for students to address questions or problems they had doing the activity. Hopefully, there will be no disparity on any of the answers to the worksheet, assuming they measured the same classroom.

Home Activity 2-2
Cost Proposal

This assignment will give you an opportunity to see if each student understands what they did in the group activity. If they have weaknesses in their understanding of dimensions and area, it will be apparent in their production.

Before they take the assignment home, each student should guess how much it would cost to recarpet and repaint their bedroom. Explain to the class that they must use complete sentences when writing and that charts, tables, or diagrams might be helpful. Their organization and proper paragraph structure is important. Also ask them to list the store or stores they called for prices. At this time, it might be helpful to review how to calculate tax on an item.

By finding out paint and carpet prices now, students will have one less item to learn about later on when they design and construct the physical model for their teen center.

Group Activity 2-2

Teen Center Name _____

Creating a Beautiful Classroom

On a separate sheet of paper answer the questions below.

Directions

Have the engineer in your group get a ruler and a yardstick. The recorder will need paper, pencil, and something on which to write.

1. What are the dimensions of the classroom?
2. How high is the ceiling?
3. What are the dimensions of each of the four walls?
4. a. How high is the doorway?
   b. How wide is the doorway?
   c. If you have windows, what are the dimensions of the window(s)?
5. a. If you were going to carpet the classroom, how many square feet of carpet would you need?
   b. How many square yards?
6. If you were going to paint the classroom, what areas would you *not* paint? Describe each area and its dimensions.
7. If you were going to paint the classroom and a gallon of paint covers 400 square feet, how many gallons, quarts, and/or pints would you need to paint the walls, not including the door?
8. Your group has decided to paint the inside door surfaces and the interior trim on the windows a different color. How much paint will you need?
9. Your group decides that after having painted the walls, one wall needs some redecoration. Your group decides to paint some geometric figures including a triangle, hexagon, circle, trapezoid, and rhombus on the wall. Figure out the dimensions and area of each of your figures and then how much paint you would need. (Make a chart.)
10. If the area of your classroom was 120 square feet and its dimensions were 10 by 12 feet, what are other possible dimensions of the room? (Make diagrams.) Which of the possible room dimensions would be the cheapest to carpet? Why?

Cost Proposal

Because of the project you did in class today, you have been inspired to redo a room at home. However, you need to convince your family that this is a worthwhile project and that you will keep the costs as low as possible.

For your cost proposal you are to do the following:

1. Measure the length and width of the room and closet, if there is one.
2. Calculate how many square yards of carpeting or tile you will need for the room and closet.
3. Find out the cost of the carpeting or tile, including sales tax, and the cost of the installation (call a local carpet or tile store).
4. Calculate the dimensions of each wall in the room and closet, and subtract the areas that will not need to be painted (describe those areas).
5. Calculate how much paint you will need if a gallon of paint covers 400 square feet (take into consideration if you will need one or two coats of paint).
6. Call a local paint store and find out the total cost of the paint.
7. Figure out the total cost of repainting and recarpeting or retiling the room and closet, including sales tax.

Finding the Area of Irregular Figures

Your students may surprise you with the variety of blueprints they will create. One of my groups created a triangular blueprint instead of a typical rectangular layout. They ended up with some rooms that were trapezoids, instead of rectangles. I had to work with them on different types of area problems. At this point, several concepts can be reviewed. Remember, your students are not architects and wise use of space is not always their priority, but being unique and different may be.

Objective
- To help students find the area of regular and irregular figures

Materials
- Graph paper $\left(\frac{1}{4} \text{ inch}\right)$
- Compass
- Ruler

Resources
- Transparency 2-3:Area
- Individual Activity 2-3:Working with Regular and Irregular Figures

 Class Activity
Regular and Irregular Figures   *40 minutes*

Review the Cartesian coordinate system. This will help students visualize the size of their rooms and use the formulas they already know.

Transparency 2-3 is a large rectangle cut up into various geometric figures. The goal of the activity is to find the total area of regions A through F.

Find the area of the large rectangular region first. The dimensions have been given (26 feet by 30 feet). The total area is 780 square feet. Using the Cartesian coordinate graph system with a $\frac{1}{4}$-inch grid provides an opportunity to talk about a scale of $\frac{1}{4}$-inch = 1 foot. Notice that there is also an opportunity to use the Pythagorean theorem and the distance formula. After a brief discussion about the area of a circle, let each group try to find Areas C though F. You can have each group prepare a transparency of a different shape. In this case, have each group present their findings orally. Each group is then responsible for taking notes while the other groups are presenting. There will be problems with Area D because Area C has to be subtracted out. Therefore, when going from group to group, be conscious of this. You might want to calculate area D with the entire class.

When the class is finished finding Areas A through F, have them total the areas. Their total areas should be close to the 780 square feet of the large rectangle. They may round some of their answers, and not get exactly 780.

Individual Activity 2-3
Working with Regular and Irregular Figures   20 minutes

This activity allows the students to work with the formulas they have just learned or reviewed in the class activity. Although this is an individual activity, I allow them to sit with their group members and discuss problems with each other.

Home Activity 2-2
Cost Proposal

Students should finish this assignment at home tonight.

Area

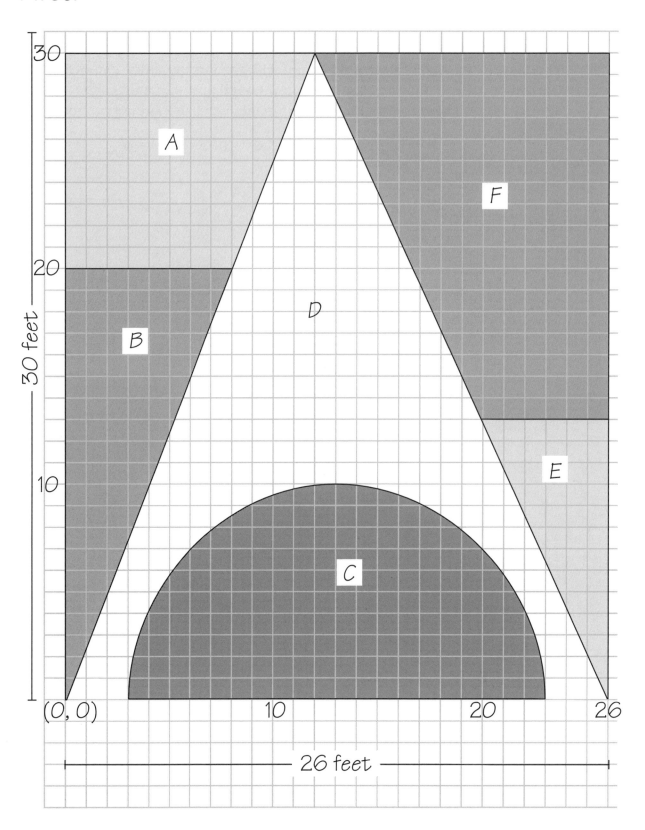

Working with Regular and Irregular Figures

1. The perimeter of an equilateral triangle is 24 feet. What is the length of each side?

2. A rectangle has a perimeter of 18 inches. Suppose the sides are integers. Graph all pairs of possible lengths l and widths w.

3. If $p = 2l + 2w$, $l = 11$ feet, and $p = 25$ feet, find w.

4. The floor plan of the following house is drawn on a coordinate system.

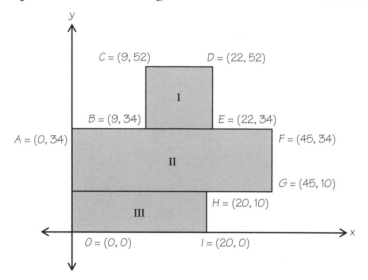

   a. Find the dimensions of rooms I, II, and III if each unit is 1 foot.
   b. What is the total floor area of the house?

5. What is the area of the trapezoid below?

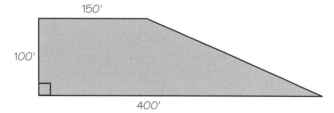

6. On graph paper, plot and connect the points $(0, 0)$, $(0, 4)$, and $(3, 0)$. What figure have you formed? What are the perimeter and area of the figure?

Working with Regular and Irregular Figures

7. *HELP* below is a square with side 9 feet, and line segment *EL* is a diameter of the circle.

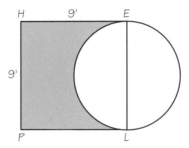

a. Find the area of the shaded region.
b. Find the perimeter of the shaded region.

An explanation of the importance of scale drawings will help the students realize what a blueprint is. Architects, automobile designers, and other professionals use blueprints. Architects have a tool called a scale that is used for scale drawings. You may want to bring one in to show students.

Objective

- To help students develop the ability to use proportion to interpret scale factors and convert units

Materials

- Graph paper $\left(\frac{1}{4} \text{ inch}\right)$
- Rulers

Resources

- Transparency 2-4: Ratio and Proportion
- Group Activity 2-4: Blueprint of the Classroom
- Home Activity 2-4: Working with Scale Drawings

 Class Activity 2-4
Making a Scale Drawing   20 minutes

You might wish to collect Home Activity 2-2: Cost Proposal before starting this class activity. Prior to introducing scale drawings, you may want to cover a few examples involving ratio. Begin the class by covering the material on Transparency 2-4.

Next, have students measure actual objects and then put them on paper using a scale drawing. They should start with something as simple as their desk. For example, their desk top could be 2 feet by 2 feet 6 inches. Have the students use the scale $\frac{1}{4}$ inch = 1 foot and draw their desk on paper. Tell them that the ratio involved is $\frac{.25 \text{ inch}}{1 \text{ foot}}$ and that they are going to set up a proportion to convert the feet to inches. They should start with the 2 feet and convert to inches and then convert 2.5 feet to inches.

$$\frac{.25}{1} = \frac{x}{2} \qquad\qquad\qquad \frac{.25}{1} = \frac{x}{2.5}$$

$$.5 = x \qquad\qquad\qquad\qquad .625 = x$$

$$\frac{1}{2} = x \qquad\qquad\qquad\qquad \frac{5}{8} = x$$

$$x = \frac{1}{2} \text{ inch} \qquad\qquad\qquad x = \frac{5}{8} \text{ inch}$$

Then ask them to draw their desk on paper but label it with the actual dimensions.

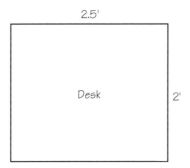

Have them find a few other objects in the room and scale them down and put on paper.

 Group Activity 2-4
Blueprint of the Classroom   15 minutes

Circulate around the room to make sure students are measuring and labeling their drawings correctly. By using a compass they can show the distance and in what direction the door opens and closes.

 Home Activity 2-4
Working with Scale Drawings

This assignment gives students the opportunity to practice solving problems that involve ratio and proportion so that they will be more comfortable with the concept when they draw their blueprints for the teen center.

Ratio and Proportion

1. Find the ratio of the area of the smaller square to the area of the larger square.

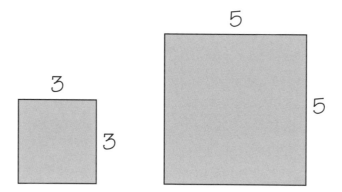

2. Refer to the rectangle and triangle in the diagram.

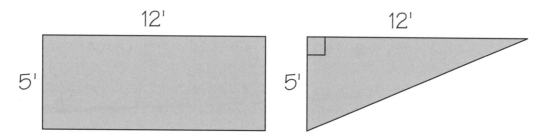

   a. Find the ratio of the perimeter of the rectangle to the perimeter of the triangle.

   b. Find the ratio of the area of the rectangle to the area of the triangle.

Blueprint of the Classroom

Directions

- Have the engineer in your group get a ruler and a yardstick.
- The recorder will need paper, pencil, and something on which to write.
- The statistician will oversee the final drawing on $\frac{1}{4}$-inch graph paper.

Note: You have some of the following dimensions from Group Activity 2-2: Creating a Beautiful Classroom.

In this activity you will use proportions to make a scale drawing of the classroom floor and one of the classroom walls.

Procedure

1. Measure the length and width of the classroom. Be sure to record your data.

2. Measure the length and width of the teacher's desk and the distance from one corner of the desk to each of the two nearest walls. Write your measurements on a sheet of paper.

3. Choose a classroom wall with several windows—or a wall with a door if no windows exist. Measure the length and height of the wall. Measure the length and height of one of the windows or door. Make the appropriate measurements to locate the position of the window or door in the wall. Using a compass, show how far the door swings open, in or out of the room. Write down your measurements.

Calculations

1. Draw the floor plan of the classroom, showing the position of the teacher's desk. To draw the floor plan, use the floor measurements you made and a scale of $\frac{1}{4}$ inch = 1 foot.

2. Using the same scale, accurately draw a wall plan using the wall and window or wall and door measurements. Make sure you include the door or windows where they belong.

Working with Scale Drawings

1. Find the ratio of the area of the smaller square to the area of the larger square.

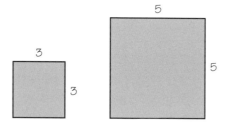

2. Refer to the rectangle and triangle in the diagram.

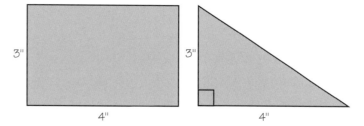

   a. Find the ratio of the perimeter of the rectangle to the perimeter of the triangle.
   b. Find the ratio of the area of the rectangle to the area of the triangle.

For Problems 3 through 5, refer to the scale diagram of a kitchen, where 1 inch = 3 feet.

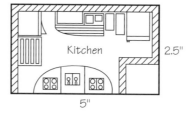

3. What are the actual dimensions of the kitchen?
4. How many square yards of linoleum are needed to cover the floor in the kitchen?
5. If linoleum costs $7.49 per square yard and the cost of installation is $85, what is the total cost of covering the floor of the kitchen with linoleum?

Lesson 2-5
Drawing the Blueprint

The time has arrived for the groups to use their knowledge about measurement and scale drawings to draw their blueprints for their teen centers. My students got so excited they could finally begin to draw their blueprints, they forgot about the paper cutouts and made many errors. They had taped sheets of graph paper together and were not too happy about starting over.

Objective

- To teach students to work in a cooperative learning environment by having them do measurement, area and perimeter, ratio and proportion, and scale drawings in order to complete a blueprint of their group's teen center

Materials

- Graph paper $\left(\frac{1}{4} \text{ inch}\right)$
- Construction paper for cutouts of rooms
- Transparent tape
- Sharp pencils
- Rulers
- Scissors
- Heavy-duty black pens

Resources

- Grade Sheet 2-5: Drawing Your Teen Center
- Group Activity 2-5: Drawing Your Teen Center Blueprint
- Home Activity 2-5: Home Floor Plan

Class Activity
Large Group Discussion   10 minutes

Take just a few minutes to go over Home Activity 2-4, because most students will probably be excited about starting their blueprints. Problems 3–5 may cause a little confusion, because the scale is $\frac{1}{4}$ inch = 3 feet. Going over these problems gives you an opportunity to see what the students learned about proportions.

The time has finally arrived for the students to start their teen center blueprints. Explain to them that they have two class periods to complete them. Suggest that they use paper cutouts of their rooms before drawing them on paper. Reemphasize that they must show actual dimensions on the blueprint and label all rooms. Explain that the scale used should be shown in the lower right-hand corner of their blueprint. Remind them to take their time taping their graph paper together so that all lines line up. Hand back their preliminary sketches from Unit 1 so that they can begin. I recommend keeping a lot of transparent tape and extra graph paper $\left(\frac{1}{4} \text{ inch}\right)$ on hand.

Note: Depending on the level of your class, you might want to give them one or two extra days to complete their blueprints.

Even though you have spent a lot of time with preliminary work, the students will still have numerous questions. Once they have their paper taped, spend some time going from group to group discussing what they are doing and making sure that they are using the scale properly. Also make sure they have taken the 9000 square feet and created the dimensions of their building. Some of my students forgot to do that.

Extension

If you can, have an architect from the community come in and spend time with each group on the development of their blueprints, but not necessarily lecturing to the class. The architect might bring in a few blueprints that she or he has done, so students can see what blueprints actually look like. This could provide an excellent opportunity to build up public relations with the community.

There are computer programs (such as CAD: computer-aided design) that do blueprints. You might want to look into the possibility of using them and working with the graphic arts teacher at your school.

Also, I suggest taking photos of your students working on their blueprints.

Assessment

While going from group to group answering questions, you might want to informally assess each student. Look for cooperative behavior, group participation, and the ability to stay on task. At this time, you might also determine whether or not the groups need more time to complete their blueprints.

For the blueprint evaluation, there is a grade sheet. Let the groups see the grade sheet before they start the blueprint. The grade sheet emphasizes the following:

- Mathematical accuracy: Does the group's scale measurements reflect their intended actual measurements? Their written report will tell you this.
- Feasibility: Could this teen center become a reality?

- Team unity: Was the blueprint a real team effort or did only one or two group members work on it?
- Timeliness
- Neatness

Home Activity 2-5
Home Floor Plan

Spend the last few minutes of class explaining that the home floor plan will be used as a form of assessment. Emphasize that they should do a neat and accurate job, just as they are doing on their teen centers, and that they have two nights to complete the assignment.

Teen Center Name _____

Names _____

Drawing Your Teen Center Blueprint

(35 points)   Mathematical Accuracy _____   Comments _____

_____

_____

(15 points)   Feasibility _____   Comments _____

_____

_____

(20 points)   Team Unity _____   Comments _____

_____

_____

(15 points)   Timeliness _____   Comments _____

_____

_____

(15 points)   Neatness _____   Comments _____

_____

_____

TOTAL POINTS _____

Drawing Your Teen Center Blueprint

Your group is now ready to draw the blueprint for your teen center. Remember to write in your daily journal. We have reviewed measurement, areas of regular and irregular figures, and ratio and proportion to prepare for this important drawing. Your final grade will reflect how well you have applied these concepts to your drawing. Keep in mind that your team unity, neatness, and promptness in preparing this blueprint will be considered in your final grade.

1 FIRST FLOOR PLAN
1/4" = 1'-0"   0'   5'   10'

The image above shows an important part of an architectural blueprint. A true blueprint is a special kind of copy made from a hand-made or computer-plotted drawing. A traditional blueprinting process uses sunlight to print an image onto sensitive paper, and ammonia to develop the image so it is readable. The ammonia causes the blue color.

Materials

The **engineer** needs to get the following:

- Several pieces of $\frac{1}{4}$-inch graph paper
- Construction paper for cutouts of rooms

Drawing Your Teen Center Blueprint

- Transparent tape
- Sharp pencils
- Rulers
- Scissors
- Heavy-duty black pens

The **statistician** should note the following:

- The teen center will be 9000 square feet.
- Scale will be $\frac{1}{4}$ inch = 1 foot and must be written on blueprint.
- Restroom dimensions will be at least 12 feet by 15 feet. (Remember to account for the requirements of Federal accessibility standards.)
- Kitchen and bathrooms will be on the same wall so that plumbing is easily accessible to both areas.
- Wall thickness will be 6 inches and must be noted on blueprint.
- All rooms are to be labeled and actual dimensions written down.
- When finished, total square footage must be accounted for.

The **recorder** should record actual dimensions and scale dimensions of each area and room.

The **project leader** needs to make sure that everyone is on task and will meet the timeline of 2 days.

Helpful Hints

- Use the dream plan you devised in Unit 1 and determine if you have enough area for the rooms you need for all the teen center activities that you would like.
- Do not forget closets and offices.
- Use paper cutouts of rooms before you draw (neatness and accuracy are extremely important).
- Draw and label in pencil first, then outline using a fairly thick black pen (your blueprints will be photographed and black shows up the best).
- Make sure your teen center name is on the blueprint.

Home Floor Plan

In this assignment, you will create a floor plan of the first floor of your home or apartment. Set up the floor plan as we did in our classroom discussion today.

Materials Needed

- Yardstick
- Ruler
- Graph paper $\left(\frac{1}{4}\text{ inch}\right)$
- Transparent tape

Directions

1. Find the dimensions of the first floor by measuring with a yardstick or tape measure.
2. Measure each room and make a rough sketch (you do not have to include closets unless you want to).
3. Include the door and how far it swings open in your sketch.
4. Include the thickness of the walls in your sketch (as part of your key).
5. Before you draw the final blueprint, make a paper cutout of each room and place the cutouts on your graph paper. Then draw in the rooms.
6. Your final drawing should include actual dimensions of each room and overall dimensions of the first floor. (**Note:** You may have to tape a few sheets of graph paper together.)

Blueprint Written Report

The blueprint written report allows you to see if the students' scale dimensions are in line with their actual dimensions and also to see what mathematical concepts they have used. It gives students an opportunity to express their feelings about working in teams and to share ideas for improving the project.

Objective

- To have the students display their knowledge of the information, concepts, and rules used in the blueprint unit

Resources

- Grade Sheet 2-6: Blueprint Written Report
- Group Activity 2-6: Blueprint Written Report
- Home Activity 2-6: Self and Group Evaluation of Teen Center Blueprint

 Group Activity 2-6
Blueprint Written Report   90 minutes

Pass out the requirements for the written report and have the groups read through them. Answer any questions and then emphasize that their reports be written with logically organized paragraphs and correct grammar, punctuation, and spelling. If you have a computer laboratory, let the recorders have a disc and then make a hard copy of their reports. With the disc, all of their reports can be saved.

Assessment

There is a grade sheet included for the written report. After the group sees their grade, keep their report in a folder. At the end of the project, they can put together a history of the project that includes the photos you have taken.

 Home Activity 2-6
Self and Group Evaluation of Teen Center Blueprint

This activity gives you an opportunity to learn from each student their thoughts on how they fit into their group, what they are learning, and their feelings in general about the project.

Grade Sheet 2-6

Teen Center Name _____

Names _____

Blueprint Written Report

(35 points)   Clarity _____   Comments _____

_____

_____

(35 points)   Accuracy _____   Comments _____

_____

_____

(15 points)   Timeliness _____   Comments _____

_____

_____

(15 points)   Neatness _____   Comments _____

_____

_____

TOTAL POINTS _____

Blueprint Written Report

Make sure that your written report is in paragraph form. Check and recheck for spelling and grammatical errors before you turn in the report. Include the following in your report:

- List your rooms and main areas. Then list the actual dimensions and scale dimensions. Here is a sample list of rooms. Feel free to add other types of rooms from your plan.

Area	Actual dimensions	Scale dimensions
Entire building		
Eating area		
Kitchen		
Restrooms		
Doorways		

- How does your group think the blueprint looks? Does it reflect your original intentions of what you wanted in your teen center?

- Write a description of the problems and/or successes your group had in making the blueprint. Describe how your group went about solving the problem.

- What suggestions would your group make to future groups that would be helpful in drawing their blueprints?

- Describe how you incorporated mathematical concepts, including measurement, ratio and proportion, and scale drawings, into the blueprint.

- Were the preliminary lessons you did in Unit 2 helpful to your group when drawing the blueprint?

- As a conclusion to your report, describe any feelings, suggestions, or comments that your group would like to make in general about this part of the project. You might want to discuss team unity, feasibility, getting work done on time, and so on.

Self and Group Evaluation of Teen Center Blueprint

Write a two-paragraph report that includes the following information:

- During the process of drawing the blueprint and writing the blueprint report, what was your role (project leader, recorder, statistician, engineer)? Explain.

- Did you feel all members of your group were equal participants? Why or why not?

- If you could grade, using A through F, what grade would you give each of the members of your group, including yourself? If this were a true business venture, would you fire anyone, including yourself? Why or why not?

- How important were the first four days of the unit in helping you succeed in drawing the blueprint? Explain.

- Did you enjoy drawing the blueprint? Why or why not?

Unit 3
Designing the Rooms

A project focus helps students develop the skills to apply mathematics to more realistic situations.

—NCTM, *A Core Curriculum*, 1992

The activities in this unit are rich in mathematics. When I started this part of the project for the first time, I thought it was just a simple vehicle to help my students build their physical models. But as I began to plan, I found I could incorporate and integrate many mathematical concepts such as matrices to set up costs for furniture, volume when we talked about air conditioning, and linear and quadratic equations for designing table arrangements.

In this unit, students design their rooms and calculate the construction costs for the interior and exterior portions of the building. The material in this unit will help students in their transition from working in two dimensions to working in three dimensions. It also provides an opportunity to bring in a contractor, plumber, electrician, or interior decorator to help them with the costs and interior designs.

I also found that when students set up their room costs, this is a good time to use a graphing calculator and/or a spreadsheet on the computer to work with matrices.

Lesson 3-3 involves quadratic and linear equations and is optional. If your students get that far in the curriculum later in the year, you might want to use this lesson at that time.

Designing the rooms and calculating all the costs that are conceivable can become detailed and complicated. Students do not need to account for everything possible in order to estimate the costs of most of the major expenses of building their teen center. Items that are left out can be considered in class discussions or activities. One way to help with prices for furniture and games is to bring in catalogs from some of the department stores and wholesale merchandisers in the area.

To help students with tables, toilets, sinks, and kitchen layouts, you can purchase templates that fit the scale $\left(\frac{1}{4}\text{ inch} = 1\text{ foot}\right)$. These are available at most office supply stores. Many of the items found on the templates, such as toilets, never became three-dimensional in my students' physical models but were just drawn on paper. Time constraints do not allow for total realism.

Mathematical Concepts

- Three-dimensional coordinate system
- Surface area
- Volume
- Linear and quadratic equations
- Matrices

Lessons

- 3-1: Three-Dimensional Coordinates
- 3-2: Volume and Surface Area
- 3-3: Linear/Quadratic Equations Based on Area (Optional)
- 3-4: Introduction to Matrices
- 3-5: Multiplication of Matrices
- 3-6: Design and Costs of Rooms Report

Assessment

Again, there is no traditional assessment, but you can use the following as assessment activities: Group Activity 3-2: Volume and Surface Area, Home Activity 3-2: Working With Surface Area and Volume, Home Activity 3-3: Finding Dimensions Again, Group Activity 3-5: Furniture Store Cost Inventory, Home Activity 3-5: More Practice with Matrices, and Group Activity 3-6: Design and Costs of Rooms Report. In fact, Group Activity 3-6 is the culmination for the unit.

Three-Dimensional Coordinates

The activities provided in this lesson give students the opportunity to visualize three dimensions using physical models and their own classroom. They can then transfer what they have seen to a three-dimensional coordinate system.

Objective

- To help students develop the ability to graph a set of points in three dimensions

Materials

- Ruler
- Graph paper $\left(\frac{1}{4} \text{ inch}\right)$
- Shoe boxes (8 or 9)
- Tape measures or yardsticks (8 or 9)
- Calculator

Resources

- Transparency 3-1a: Coordinates in Three Dimensions
- Transparency 3-1b: Graphing a Plane
- Group Activity 3-1: Objects in the Classroom
- Home Activity 3-1: Graphing Three-Dimensional Coordinates

Class Activity 3-1
Graphing in Three Dimensions   20 minutes

Since the students will be working in three dimensions when they design their rooms and when they build their physical models (Unit 6), this is an opportune time to introduce a three-dimensional coordinate system. Objects and points in a room can be located and placed more appropriately with an understanding of a three-dimensional coordinate system.

To introduce the three-dimensional coordinate system, have each group bring in a shoe box.

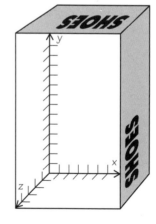

Using a magic marker, the students mark the *x*-, *y*-, and *z*-axes and label the planes. This will help them to visualize the three-dimensional coordinate system.

Transparency 3-1a
Coordinates in Three Dimensions

Use Transparency 3-1a to show how to draw a three-dimensional coordinate system on a two-dimensional plane. Show that the *x*-axis makes a 45-degree angle with the other two axes. Also, the scale of the *x*-axis should be about 70% of the other two axes. This way the *x*-axis will appear to have the right proportions in relation to the *y*- and *z*-axes. It might be easier to draw the *y*- and *z*-axes using one unit and the *x*-axis using two units.

Transparency 3-1a also shows how to draw the coordinate system and plot a point. This is an opportunity to tell the students that the point $R = (-2, 4, 6)$ is called an ordered triple, not an ordered pair. In addition, this transparency shows how a quadrilateral that is a rectangle can be graphed. After graphing the rectangle, the students can find the area.

Transparency 3-1b
Graphing a Plane

Transparency 3-1b shows that a graph with three variables is a plane in space. It gives the students an opportunity to find the three traces and the three intercepts. When they look at the triangle they have just drawn, it should almost look three-dimensional.

Group Activity 3-1
Objects in the Classroom   *30 minutes*

With this activity, students have an opportunity to visualize objects in the classroom and then graph them on a three-dimensional coordinate system. Let one corner of the room be the origin. Then, by using the two coordinates *x* and *y*, demonstrate that the location of an object on the floor can be defined using an ordered pair. To demonstrate the need for a third dimension, have students try to use two coordinates to locate two objects that have the same *x*- and *y*- coordinates but different heights. When I used this activity, I had my classes play a game by guessing which objects different groups were describing. It helped show the importance of being accurate when measuring. Before starting the activity, I had already picked out a few objects in the room to use as examples.

Home Activity 3-1
Graphing Three-Dimensional Coordinates

This is an opportunity to practice graphing in three dimensions. Since there is a volume question, it may be appropriate to review how to find volume after you hand out the worksheet.

Coordinates in Three Dimensions

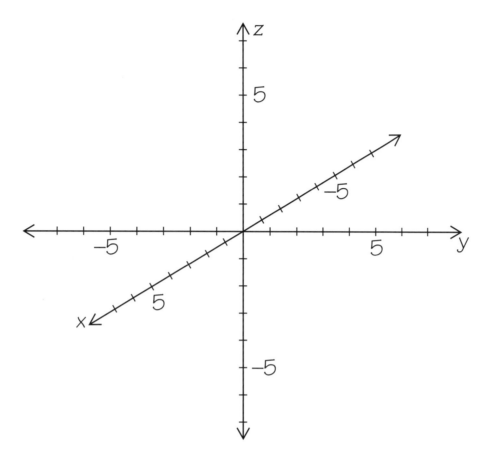

1. Plot the point $R = (-2, 4, 6)$ on a three-dimensional coordinate system.

   Answer: x-coordinate is -2, so slide 2 units back (in a negative direction) on x-axis; y-coordinate is 4, so move 4 units in positive direction parallel to y-axis; and since z-coordinate is 6, go 6 units up parallel to z-axis.

Coordinates in Three Dimensions

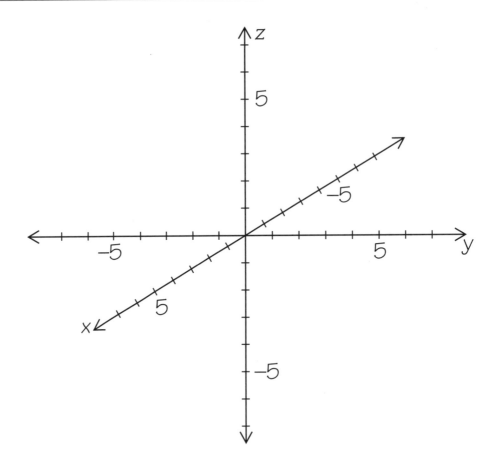

2. Draw the quadrilateral that has vertices $(3, 0, 0)$, $(3, 7, 0), (0, 7, 0)$, and $(0, 0, 0)$.

   What type of quadrilateral is this?
   Answer: rectangle

   What is its area?
   Answer: 21 square units

   Name the plane in which it lies.
   Answer: xy-plane

Graphing a Plane

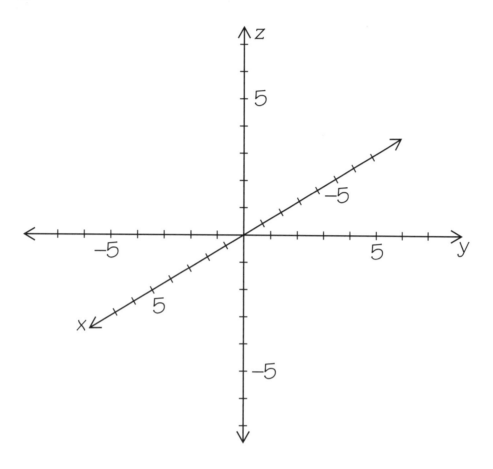

1. Plot the equation $3x + 4y + 6z = 12$.

2. Find the x- y- and z- intercepts and plot the intercepts.

   Answer:
   By setting y and $z = 0, x = 4$.
   By setting x and $z = 0, y = 3$.
   By setting x and $y = 0, z = 2$.

3. Show the traces.

   Answer:
   By setting $x = 0$, the yz trace is $4y + 6z = 12$.
   By setting $y = 0$, the xz trace is $3x + 6z = 12$.
   By setting $z = 0$, the xy trace is $3x + 4y = 12$.

Objects in the Classroom

Use the following diagram to locate objects in the classroom. Let the origin be a corner of the classroom.

1. Create a scale for the units used in the coordinate system.

2. Estimate the coordinates of three points on the floor. Make sure you describe the points and then make a graph to represent each point.

3. Estimate the coordinates of the doorknob.

4. Estimate the coordinates of three points *not* on the floor. Make sure you describe the points and then make a graph to represent each point.

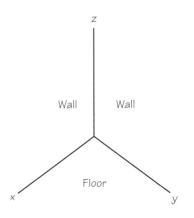

Building a Teen Center
©1998 Key Curriculum Press

Graphing Three-Dimensional Coordinates

Use a sheet of graph paper to answer the questions below.

1. Plot the following points: $A = (1, 3, -2)$ and $B = (0, -2, 4)$.

2. A box has the following vertices: the origin, $(4, 0, 0)$, $(4, 5, 0)$, $(0, 5, 0)$, $(0, 5, 6)$, $(0, 0, 6)$, $(4, 0, 6)$, and $(4, 5, 6)$.
   a. Plot the points and draw the box.
   b. Determine the volume of the box.
   c. Determine the surface area of the box.

3. Sketch a graph of the following by drawing its three traces.
   a. $2x - 3y + 2z = 12$
   b. $3x + 5y - 5z = 15$

The discussion of air conditioning is a real-world application for learning the concept of volume. I also included activities in this lesson in which students find the volume of rectangular solids. Some of my groups put stereo systems, video games, dishwashers, refrigerators, and stages in their physical models and needed to understand the concept of volume to make scale models of these.

Although surface area was discussed in Unit 2, it has been included again in this section. Students will need to understand how to calculate surface area to calculate costs of painting and carpeting or tiling the teen center.

Objective

- To help students develop the ability to calculate the volume and surface area for a rectangular solid

Materials

- Rulers
- Scissors
- Graph paper $\left(\frac{1}{4} \text{ inch}\right)$
- Transparent tape
- Calculator

Resources

- Transparency 3-2: Air Exchange
- Group Activity 3-2: Volume and Surface Area
- Home Activity 3-2: Working with Surface Area and Volume

 Class Activity 3-2
Air Exchange   10 minutes

You can start with a discussion of Home Activity 3-1. Focus on Problem 2 on volume and surface area, and use Problem 2 as a lead-in to Lesson 3-2. Use Transparency 3-2 to present the relationship of air conditioning to volume.

 Group Activity 3-2
Volume and Surface Area   30 minutes

This activity has two parts. In the first part, students will repeat the air-exchange activity from Class Activity 3-2 using their classroom and the number of students in their class. In the second part of the activity, students will build different rectangular solids out of paper and then calculate the volume, calculate the surface area, and convert scale dimensions to actual dimensions for each solid. This will help them when they construct the physical model of their teen center (Unit 6).

Note: There is an opportunity to expand this activity by writing an equation of a cubic function, graphing it on a graphing calculator, and finding its x- and y- intercepts.

Home Activity 3-2
Working with Surface Area and Volume

This assignment gives each student the opportunity to practice finding volume and surface area. It also gives them further practice calculating paint and carpet costs. They can save the refrigerator and pool-table models that they make out of paper to include in their physical models (Unit 6).

When I first did this project with my students they were so excited to make video games, pool tables, and regular tables that they lost focus when it came to accuracy.

Air Exchange

A common guideline for air exchange in a school classroom is for the air conditioning to supply about 1600 cubic feet of air per occupant every hour. Suppose a classroom is designed to hold 20 occupants (students). The room is rectangular, 20 feet across the front and 40 feet from front to back, and the walls are 10 feet high.

1. How much air should be supplied each hour for 20 students in the classroom?

   Answer:

   Air for students = Air per hour per student
   $\qquad\qquad\qquad\qquad$ × Number of students

   $\qquad\qquad$ = 1600 cubic feet per hour
   $\qquad\qquad\qquad$ per student × 20 students

   $\qquad\qquad$ = 32,000 cubic feet per hour

2. What is the volume of air in the classroom? (Actually the volume of the occupants should be deducted from this volume. Ignore this for the exercise.)

   Answer:

   Volume of classroom = Length × Width × Height

   $\qquad\qquad\qquad\qquad$ = 40 × 20 × 10

   $\qquad\qquad\qquad\qquad$ = 8000 cubic feet

Air Exchange

3. How many times each hour should the air volume in the classroom be replenished by the air conditioning?

Answer:

Roomfuls of air = Air needed per hour
                    ÷ Volume of room

= 32,000 cubic feet per hour
    ÷ 8000 cubic feet per room

= 4 roomfuls per hour

The air will be replenished four times each hour.

Volume and Surface Area

1. Refer back to Group Activity 2-2 and find the length, width, and height of your classroom.
   a. How much air should be supplied each hour for the number of students in your classroom?
   b. What is the volume of air in your classroom?
   c. How many times each hour should the air volume in your classroom be replenished?
2. You will need graph paper and scissors for this activity.
   a. Cut four 10-unit by 20-unit rectangles from your graph paper. (Have each group member cut a different rectangle.)

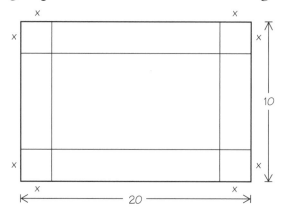

   b. Construct four open-top boxes with different x-value dimensions. Construct the boxes by cutting a square from each corner and folding up the sides. Then cut out a top and tape it over the open space so that the open-top box becomes a rectangular solid.
   c. Fill in the following table. Remember $\frac{1}{4}$ inch = 1 foot.

Scale			Actual		
Dimensions	Volume	Surface Area	Dimensions	Volume	Surface Area

Working with Surface Area and Volume

1. A dining room is 18 feet long, 16 feet wide, and 8 feet high. Find the total area of the walls, floor, and ceiling, allowing 120 square feet for the windows and the door. If 1 gallon of paint covers 360 square feet with one coat, how many gallons will be needed to cover the walls, floor, and ceiling with two coats? Round the answer to the nearest gallon. If 1 gallon of paint costs $9.85, how much will it cost for paint to cover the walls, floor, and ceiling with two coats of paint?

2. Suppose that the air-conditioning system in your bedroom moves 800 cubic feet of air per minute. How long will it take to replace the air in your bedroom? You need to find the dimensions in order to figure out the volume of your bedroom.

3. Find the volume of your refrigerator. Then build a miniature model of it using graph paper and a scale of $\frac{1}{4}$ inch = 1 foot.

4. Your teen center has a stage. Make a miniature model of your stage using graph paper and a scale of $\frac{1}{4}$ inch = 1 foot.

5. Find out the dimensions of a pool table. Then make a miniature model of it using graph paper and a scale of $\frac{1}{4}$ inch = 1 foot.

6. Consider the equations $2x + 5y + 10z = 20$ and $2x + 5y + 10z = 30$.
    a. Graph the equations on graph paper on the same set of axes.
    b. What do you notice about the planes?

Linear/Quadratic Equations
Based on Area

The main activity to be used in this lesson, "Al Gebra's Night Club," is the reason I became inspired to write this entire project. Bob Davis wrote this activity for "Opening the Gate" (Algebra for All supplementary activities for the state of Florida). "Al Gebra's Night Club" provides an opportunity to use linear and quadratic equations to calculate area dimensions. The activity is very appropriate for the teen center project in general because it involves table arrangements with relation to the wall and other tables. I approach this particular activity using the graphing calculator. However, if you give the activity to your students who have limited experience with quadratic equations, they most likely will be able to figure out the problem without using any equations. They will find a pattern and use guess-and-check. I have seen many groups in my own classes take this approach even after having a full unit on quadratic expressions and equations.

You may want to do your entire unit on quadratics before approaching the activity, but I have developed a class activity and a home activity revolving around particular word problems that are as relevant to the teen center as possible. Finding the solutions will not require factoring or the quadratic formula, but will involve using the graphing calculator. The graphing calculator I use is the TI-82.

Objective
- To help students develop the ability to solve quadratic functions using graphs of quadratic equations

Materials
- Overhead graphing calculator
- Classroom set of graphing calculators
- Graph paper $\left(\frac{1}{4}\ \text{inch}\right)$

Resources
- Transparency 3-3: Finding Dimensions
- Class Activity 3-3: Finding Dimensions
- Group Activity 3-3: Al Gebra's Night Club
- Home Activity 3-3: Finding Dimensions Again

Class Activity 3-3
Finding Dimensions
15 minutes

Before starting Lesson 3-3, review Home Activity 3-2. One way to do this is to make an answer sheet for each group and then, while you are taking attendance and doing other paper work, the groups can start checking their homework. Circulate around the room, checking whether the homework was completed and answering any questions. For this exercise, look at their paper rectangular solids to see how accurately they converted actual dimensions to scale dimensions. The groups can save their refrigerator and pool-table models for use later on when they build the physical models.

Hand out Class Activity 3-3: Finding Dimensions to each student so that they can follow along with you. If you have two overhead projectors, use one for Transparency 3-3: Finding Dimensions and use the other for the overhead calculator. The graphing calculator opens an interesting door and can even motivate students who have very little experience with quadratic functions to want to learn more about them.

Group Activity 3-3
Al Gebra's Night Club
60 minutes

I have made a few revisions, but basically Bob Davis's activity is intact. There are multiple ways the dimensions can be found. Again, depending on the background of your class, their solutions and methods can be quite interesting. One suggestion is to have the students conquer the activity with very little quadratic function experience and then redo the activity later in the year after they have had an entire unit on quadratics.

Home Activity 3-3
Finding Dimensions Again

There is only one problem and it is essentially the same as the one done in the class activity. It is important that students have access to a graphing calculator in order to simulate and practice what they did in class.

Finding Dimensions

Club Wisdom, the local teen center, wishes to put up a display area. It will be a rectangular area enclosed on three sides by glass and the fourth side will be an existing wall. The center wants to use 50 yards of glass to create the display area that encloses the maximum area. What should the dimensions be?

There are 50 yards of glass and the enclosure will have three walls.

Let x be the distance the display area extends from the wall, in yards.

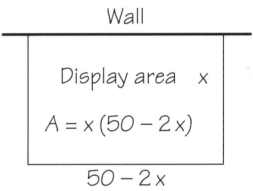

Wall

Display area   x

$A = x(50 - 2x)$

$50 - 2x$

Let 50 – 2x be the other dimension.

Then the equation for the area of the display is $y = x(50 - 2x)$.

Using a graphing calculator:

Enter functions   Set window   See graph

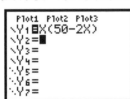

Answer: The maximum appears to be very close to $x = 12.5$.

The maximum area that can be enclosed by the glass is about 312 square yards. So these dimensions maximize the area: a width of 12.5 feet, and a length of 25 feet.

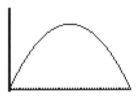

Finding Dimensions

Club Wisdom, the local teen center, wishes to put up a display area. It will be a rectangular area enclosed on three sides by glass and the fourth side will be an existing wall. The center wants to use 50 yards of glass to create the display area that encloses the maximum area. What should the dimensions be?

There are 50 yards of glass and the enclosure will have three walls.

Let x be the distance the display area extends from the wall, in yards.

Let $50 - 2x$ be the other dimension.

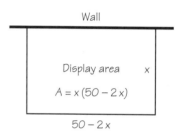

Wall

Display area x

$A = x\,(50 - 2x)$

$50 - 2x$

Al Gebra's Nightclub

Mr. Al Gebra decided to use the profits from another company with which he was very successful to open a teen center. After studying much statistical data, Al surmised that this club should seat a minimum of 1152 people at tables. The tables will be 3 feet by 6 feet, and each one will seat 6 customers. Fire codes require that all tables be at least 3 feet from the wall and that there be at least a 3-foot space between tables. There must be a 6-foot walkway through the center of the room parallel to the width of the building.

Al must now decide on the dimensions of the building. Assuming the length of the building will be twice the width, find the dimensions of the smallest possible building Al can construct. Also, describe the arrangement of the tables in the building.

1. On graph paper, sketch your teen center including the table arrangement. Label all dimensions.

2. Write a summary of your problem-solving procedure. Be specific.

3. List all equations or inequalities used. Be sure to define any variables and/or expressions.

Building a Teen Center
©1998 Key Curriculum Press

Finding Dimensions Again

Club Wisdom, the local teen center, wishes to put up a larger display area. It will be a rectangular area enclosed on three sides by glass and the fourth side will be an existing wall. If the center wants to use 60 yards of glass to create the display area that encloses the maximum area, what should the dimensions be? Make sure you do the following:

1. Define all variables and expressions.

2. Make a sketch of the display area.

3. Write down your calculator entries including the window used.

4. Using graph paper, make a sketch of the graph from your calculator that includes the x-coordinates and the coordinates where the area is maximized.

5. Draw a diagram of the display area showing the final dimensions.

Introduction to Matrices

I found that calculating the costs of the furniture, pool tables, stereos, video games, and other items that would be going into the various rooms of the teen center provided an excellent opportunity to teach matrices.

This lesson revolves around adding and subtracting matrices and equivalent matrices. The lesson also shows the students how to enter the matrices into their graphing calculator (TI-82) and perform the various operations.

Objective
- To help students develop the ability to add and subtract matrices

Materials
- Overhead graphing calculator
- Classroom set of graphing calculators

Resources
- Transparency 3-4: Inventory and Prices
- Group Activity 3-4: Introducing Matrices
- Home Activity 3-4: Practice Using Matrices

 **Group Activity 3-4**
Introducing Matrices   *40 minutes*

Students should have this worksheet as well as a graphing calculator. If you have two overhead projectors, use one for Transparency 3-4 and the other for the overhead calculator.

Begin the lesson by stating that Club Wisdom's owner, Andrea, is interested in buying tables for her teen center but is also interested in learning about how to keep an inventory for her teen center. So she visits a local furniture store. She learns that matrices are used to record the store's inventory. At this time, explain that a matrix is the same as a table or a spreadsheet. Introduce the vocabulary involved: elements, rows, and columns.

The worksheet starts with the number of tables in stock (Current Inventory Matrix) and then a delivery is made (Additional Inventory for Restock). The students have to add the two matrices together in order to get the new inventory after the store has been restocked (Inventory After Restock).

Andrea revisits the store a few weeks later to find out how many tables have been sold. Here, the matrices must be subtracted.

Inventory After Restock Matrix − Sales Matrix = Inventory After Sales Matrix.

Andrea is also interested in mark-up. To introduce scalar multiplication, I created a Buying Price Matrix. The store marks up its prices 2.5 times. So, 2.5 × Buying Price Matrix = Sales Price Matrix.

The transparency includes only the matrices. The worksheet includes all information needed.

Home Activity 3-4
Practicing Using Matrices

It would be advantageous if the students could take home their graphing calculators to practice on when doing their homework. The practice exercises are pretty straightforward and can be done without a graphing calculator. But knowing how to use a graphing calculator is still a helpful skill.

Inventory and Prices

Current Inventory

Brand	Large	Medium	Small
MacWard	30	20	10
Sparky's	25	35	15
Laritz	40	30	10
Baydines	40	50	30

Additional Inventory for Restock

Brand	Large	Medium	Small
MacWard	14	12	10
Sparky's	22	18	16
Laritz	10	12	17
Baydines	40	7	50

Inventory After Restock

Brand	Large	Medium	Small
MacWard	30 + 14		
Sparky's			
Laritz			
Baydines			

Building a Teen Center
©1998 Key Curriculum Press

Inventory and Prices

Sales

Brand	Large	Medium	Small
MacWard	15	12	7
Sparky's	38	24	13
Laritz	6	17	8
Baydines	18	40	19

Inventory After Sales

Brand	Large	Medium	Small
MacWard	44 − 15		
Sparky's			
Laritz			
Baydines			

Inventory and Prices

Wholesale Costs

Brand	Large	Medium	Small
MacWard	$25.75	$20.75	$15.75
Sparky's	$28.95	$23.95	$18.95
Laritz	$32.80	$25.80	$21.80
Baydines	$40.00	$35.00	$30.00

Retail Prices

Brand	Large	Medium	Small
MacWard			
Sparky's			
Laritz			
Baydines			

Introducing Matrices

A **matrix** is an array of numbers arranged in rows and columns. The table of furniture store inventory shown below is a 4×3 matrix of numbers. It has four rows and three columns. Each element of the matrix can be referred to by row and column. For example, the ordered pair $A(3, 1) = 40$. If you look at the table, row 3 column 1 shows that Laritz has 40 large tables.

What would happen if a new shipment of tables was delivered to the furniture store? There would be a packing list to let the store know what was being delivered. The next matrix represents the packing list to restock the store. Use the Current Inventory matrix and the Additional Inventory for Restock matrix to complete the Inventory After Restock table.

Current Inventory

Brand	Large	Medium	Small
MacWard	30	20	10
Sparky's	25	35	15
Laritz	40	30	10
Baydines	40	50	30

Additional Inventory for Restock

Brand	Large	Medium	Small
MacWard	14	12	10
Sparky's	22	18	16
Laritz	10	12	17
Baydines	40	7	50

To calculate the inventory after restock, add the corresponding elements of the matrix.

Inventory After Restock

Brand	Large	Medium	Small
MacWard	30 + 14		
Sparky's			
Laritz			
Baydines			

To do the same thing using matrix notation see the example below. Matrices are usually denoted with capital letters.

Inventory   **Inventory After Restock**   **Final Inventory**

$$A = \begin{bmatrix} 14 & 12 & 10 \\ 22 & 18 & 16 \\ 10 & 12 & 17 \\ 40 & 7 & 50 \end{bmatrix} \quad B = \begin{bmatrix} 30 & 20 & 10 \\ 25 & 35 & 15 \\ 40 & 30 & 10 \\ 40 & 50 & 30 \end{bmatrix} \quad A + B = \begin{bmatrix} 14+30 & 12+20 & 10+10 \\ & & \\ & & \\ & & \end{bmatrix} = C$$

Introducing Matrices

The reason for this notation is that an entire table can be represented using one variable. In this activity you will learn to add and subtract matrices.

The purpose of any store is to sell its inventory, so when Andrea came back to visit in February she was curious to see how many tables had been sold. The following matrix represents the February sales.

Sales

Brand	Large	Medium	Small
MacWard	15	12	7
Sparky's	38	24	13
Laritz	6	17	8
Baydines	18	40	19

Inventory After Sales

Brand	Large	Medium	Small
MacWard	44 − 15		
Sparky's			
Laritz			
Baydines			

To get the Inventory After Sales:

Inventory After Restock (end of January) − Sales Inventory (February) = Inventory After Sales.

Try using a graphing calculator or spreadsheet program to enter these matrices.

Club Wisdom will be selling food and soft drinks, so Andrea is interested in mark-up. She talks to the store manager so that she can learn more about mark-up. The furniture store buys its tables for a certain price and then marks up the tables to 2.5 times their buying price. How can Andrea find the retail price?

Wholesale Costs

Brand	Large	Medium	Small
MacWard	$25.75	$20.75	$15.75
Sparky's	$28.95	$23.95	$18.95
Laritz	$32.80	$25.80	$21.80
Baydines	$40.00	$35.00	$30.00

Retail Prices

Brand	Large	Medium	Small
MacWard			
Sparky's			
Laritz			
Baydines			

Multiplying a matrix by a number is called **scalar multiplication**. To do this, multiply each element of the matrix by the scalar.

$$2.5 \begin{bmatrix} 25.75 & 20.75 & 15.75 \\ 28.95 & 23.95 & 18.95 \\ 32.80 & 25.80 & 21.80 \\ 40 & 35 & 30 \end{bmatrix} = \begin{bmatrix} 64.38 & 51.88 & 39.38 \\ 72.38 & 59.88 & 47.38 \\ 82 & 64.50 & 54.50 \\ 100 & 87.50 & 75 \end{bmatrix}$$

Practice Using Matrices

1. The matrix below shows the wages of several employees. What scalar multiplier should be used to produce a product matrix representing the employees' wages after a 15% pay raise? Multiply the matrix below to calculate the wages after the increase.

$$A = \begin{bmatrix} 46{,}000 & 23{,}000 & 19{,}000 \\ 49{,}000 & 25{,}000 & 21{,}000 \\ 53{,}000 & 29{,}000 & 24{,}000 \end{bmatrix}$$

In Problems 2 through 7, use the following matrices to find the sums or the differences.

$$A = \begin{bmatrix} -4 & 2 & -1 \\ 6 & 5 & -3 \\ 1 & 8 & 9 \end{bmatrix} \quad B = \begin{bmatrix} -6 & 4 & 2 \\ 9 & -7 & 5 \\ -2 & 3 & 10 \end{bmatrix}$$

2. $A - B$

3. $A + B$

4. $B - A$

5. $0.5A + B$

6. $7B - 4A$

7. $B + 3A$

8. The following are equivalent matrices. What do you think equivalent matrices are? See if you can find what the variables are. The values of the variables stay the same throughout the exercise and you need to find a before you find b, and so on.

$$\begin{bmatrix} 2a & a+3 & c & 2l \\ 26 & f & 2b-1 & h \\ \frac{c}{b} & j & 31 & 18 \\ \frac{m}{2} & 3 & o & 30 \end{bmatrix} = \begin{bmatrix} 4 & b & b-1 & 2d \\ 2e+a & 2l & g & 3a \\ i & 2c-b & 3k+1 & 2l-4 \\ 4 & n+2 & 2b-k & p+11 \end{bmatrix}$$

In this lesson students learn how to multiply with 2×2 and 2×1 matrices. Students can also use graphing calculators to enter the matrices and perform the multiplication process, because multiplying large matrices can become tedious.

Objective
- To help students develop the ability to multiply matrices

Materials
- Overhead graphing calculator
- Classroom set of graphing calculators
- Two overhead projectors

Resources
- Transparency 3-5: Matrix Multiplication
- Class Activity 3-5: Multiplying Matrices
- Group Activity 3-5: Furniture Store Cost Inventory
- Home Activity 3-5: More Practice with Matrices

Class Activity 3-5
Multiplying Matrices   40 minutes

Have the groups check their homework and circulate to see if they have completed it. A small discussion here about the equivalent matrices problem might be warranted before they start to learn to multiply matrices.

The furniture store, mentioned in Lesson 3–4, is going to make banners to advertise some new tables they purchased and wish to sell at a sale price. Luis and Evelyn have the task of making the banners. Transparency 3-5 shows the matrices used, but the students will need to follow along with their own worksheets. The worksheet is much more detailed than the transparency. Again, you might want to use two overhead projectors. (One projector is for the overhead calculator and the other is for the transparency.)

Distribute the worksheets and allow the students time to work on their calculations before beginning the discussion. Students need to discover that the number of columns in the first matrix must match the number of rows in the second matrix in order for multiplication to be possible.

This process will require patience because they are just learning how to do it. After they have been introduced to the process and can explain the procedure, show them how to multiply matrices using the calculator.

Note: Tell the students that when multiplying matrices using the calculator, they should not put a multiplication sign between the matrices. If they do, an error will occur.

 ## Group Activity 3-5
Furniture Store Cost Inventory   *60 minutes*

This activity gives each group the opportunity to apply their knowledge about matrices by calculating inventory cost. They will work with store cost, customer cost, and a little with profits. Encourage them to use the calculator to multiply matrices.

 ## Home Activity 3-5
More Practice with Matrices

There are word problems in this exercise, along with straight multiplication. Hopefully students can take the calculators home because of the use of 4×4 matrices. Without calculators, the assignment will be long and tedious for them.

Matrix Multiplication

Banner Matrix

	Large	Medium
Luis	15	10
Evelyn	10	8

Material Matrix

	Blue	Green
Large	4	3
Medium	2	1

Result Matrix

Name × Color (Strips Matrix)

	Blue	Green
Luis	80	55
Evelyn	56	38

Matrix Multiplication

$$\begin{bmatrix} a & b \\ c & d \end{bmatrix} \cdot \begin{bmatrix} e & f \\ g & h \end{bmatrix} = \begin{bmatrix} a \cdot e + b \cdot g & a \cdot f + b \cdot h \\ c \cdot e + d \cdot g & c \cdot f + d \cdot h \end{bmatrix}$$

$$\begin{bmatrix} 15 & 10 \\ 10 & 8 \end{bmatrix} \cdot \begin{bmatrix} 4 & 3 \\ 2 & 1 \end{bmatrix} = \begin{bmatrix} 15 \cdot 4 + 10 \cdot 2 & 15 \cdot 3 + 10 \cdot 1 \\ 10 \cdot 4 + 8 \cdot 2 & 10 \cdot 3 + 8 \cdot 1 \end{bmatrix}$$

Result Matrix · Cost Matrix = Expense Matrix

	Blue	Green
Luis	80	55
Evelyn	56	38

$\cdot$

Blue	0.75
Green	0.55

$=$

$90.25
$62.90

Multiplying Matrices

In this activity you will learn to multiply two matrices. When you multiply two matrices you must match corresponding rows and columns, multiply them together, and then add them. It can get complicated when you start working with large matrices. Consider the example below.

The furniture store is going to make banners to advertise some new tables it purchased and wishes to sell. Luis and Evelyn have the task of making the banners. The banners feature the store colors, blue and green. The first table shows how many large and medium banners Luis and Evelyn are expected to make. For example, Luis must make 15 large banners and 10 medium banners. The second table shows how many strips of each color fabric are required for each banner. For example, to make a large banner Luis and Evelyn need 4 strips of blue fabric and 3 strips of green. To make a medium banner they need 2 strips of blue fabric and 1 strip of green.

Banner Matrix

	Large	Medium
Luis	15	10
Evelyn	10	8

Fabric Matrix

	Blue	Green
Large	4	3
Medium	2	1

1. How many strips of blue fabric will Luis need to make all of his banners?

2. How many strips of green fabric will Luis need to make all of his banners?

3. How many strips of blue fabric will Evelyn need to make all of her banners?

4. How many strips of green fabric will Evelyn need to make all of her banners?

5. Record the answers to Problems 1 through 4 in a result matrix. The operation you just performed is **matrix multiplication**. You calculated **Banner Matrix • Fabric Matrix = Result Matrix**.

6. Now, finish the following exercise to see if you understand the process of matrix multiplication.

$$\begin{bmatrix} a & b \\ c & d \end{bmatrix} \cdot \begin{bmatrix} e & f \\ g & h \end{bmatrix} = \begin{bmatrix} a \cdot e + b \cdot g & a \cdot f + b \cdot h \\ c \cdot e + d \cdot g & \underline{\hspace{2cm}} \end{bmatrix}$$

7. Luis's and Evelyn's banners are going to cost $0.75 per strip for the blue and $0.55 per strip for the green, so a **cost matrix** needs to be set up.

   Cost Matrix

   $$\begin{array}{c}\text{Blue} \\ \text{Green}\end{array}\begin{bmatrix}\$0.75 \\ \$0.55\end{bmatrix}$$

   The result matrix needs to be multiplied by the cost matrix to get the **expense matrix**.

   Result Matrix · Cost Matrix = Expense Matrix

   $$\begin{array}{c}\quad \\ \text{Luis} \\ \text{Evelyn}\end{array}\begin{array}{c}\text{Blue} \quad \text{Green} \\ \begin{bmatrix}80 & 55 \\ 56 & 38\end{bmatrix}\end{array} \cdot \begin{array}{c}\quad \\ \text{Blue} \\ \text{Green}\end{array}\begin{bmatrix}.75 \\ .55\end{bmatrix} = \begin{bmatrix}\quad \\ \quad\end{bmatrix}$$

8. How would you describe the cost matrix?

9. How much will it cost Luis to make his banners?

10. How much will it cost Evelyn to make her banners?

11. How would you describe the expense matrix?

Building a Teen Center
©1998 Key Curriculum Press

Furniture Store Cost Inventory

Here is the inventory matrix for our furniture store. The furniture store pays its supplier $20 for each small table, $25 for each medium table, and $30 for each large table. Make a matrix with this information and name it Store Cost. Then use it to calculate **Store Inventory · Store Cost = Stock Value**. The Stock Value matrix tells what it costs the furniture store to keep each table in stock.

Store Inventory

Brand	Large	Medium	Small
MacWard	15	12	7
Sparky's	38	24	13
Laritz	6	17	8
Baydines	18	40	19

Store Costs

Size	Cost
Large	$30
Medium	$25
Small	$20

Total Value of Stock

MacWard	$15 \times \$30 + 12 \times \$25 + 7 \times \$20 = \$890$
Sparky's	
Laritz	
Baydines	

Here is the September Sales matrix for the furniture store.

Sales

Brand	Large	Medium	Small
MacWard	8	2	4
Sparky's	21	14	8
Laritz	3	12	2
Baydines	7	21	12

Retail Prices

Size	Cost
Large	$55
Medium	$47
Small	$32

Multiply the above matrices to calculate the retail income from the September sales.

Furniture Store Cost Inventory

Total Sales Income

MacWard	$8 \times \$55 + 2 \times \$47 + 4 \times \$32 = \$662$
Sparky's	
Laritz	
Baydines	

Use the Sales Value and the Stock Value matrices to find the store's September profit on the tables. What operation will you use?

Home Activity 3-5

Name _____

More Practice with Matrices

1. The following matrices show the number of miles driven in a year by each member of a family and the cost per mile of driving each of the family's cars (including gas, insurance, license fees, and so on).

Miles Driven

	Car 1	Car 2
Mother	4537	2358
Father	6547	3475
Child 1	1579	1298
Child 2	3543	1579

Cost per Mile (dollars)

Car 1	0.18
Car 2	0.29

   a. What is the cost of each person's driving?
   b. What is the total cost of the family's driving?
   c. How much would the family have saved if child 1 had always driven car 1?

2. Find each product.

   a. $\begin{bmatrix} 5 & -8 \\ 2 & 6 \end{bmatrix} \begin{bmatrix} -3 & 4 \\ 7 & 9 \end{bmatrix}$
   b. $\begin{bmatrix} 5 & -8 \\ 2 & 6 \end{bmatrix} \begin{bmatrix} 7 & 9 \\ -3 & 4 \end{bmatrix}$
   c. $\begin{bmatrix} 5 & -8 \\ 2 & 6 \end{bmatrix} \begin{bmatrix} 4 & -3 \\ 9 & 7 \end{bmatrix}$

3. You are about to buy furniture and video games for your teen center, so you decide to develop the first matrix below, which shows the quantity of each type of furniture that will go in a room. The second matrix shows the price of each item. What would your total expenses be for furniture?

Quantity

Room	Couches	Tables	Desks	Chairs	Games
Dining	2	0	0	100	0
Game	2	0	0	8	5
Kitchen	0	2	0	8	0
Office	1	0	3	5	0

Price per Item

Item	Price
Couch	$300
Table	$60
Desk	$250
Chair	$20
Game	$500

Design and Costs of Rooms Report

The time has arrived to design the rooms and calculate the costs for the various pieces of furniture and games planned for the teen center rooms. The only activity in this lesson is the group activity.

Objective

- To help students develop the ability to integrate the mathematical concepts of three dimensions, volume, surface area, linear and quadratic equations, and matrices

Materials

- Ruler
- Graph paper $\left(\frac{1}{4} \text{ inch}\right)$
- Transparent tape
- Store catalogs
- Graphing calculator

Resource

- Grade Sheet 3-6: Design and Costs of Rooms Report
- Group Activity 3-6: Design and Costs of Rooms Report

 Group Activity 3-6
Design and Costs of Rooms Report   160 minutes

In this activity students design their rooms and decide what they want in them. They also need to calculate construction costs, exterior expenses (for example, paint), and interior expenses (furniture, paint/wallpaper, carpet/tile, restroom fixtures, and so on). They need to bring in catalogs from various department stores to do their shopping. All of these items and their costs should all be included in a written report. There is an evaluation sheet included for grading their written reports.

Teen Center Name _____

Names _____

Design and Costs of Rooms Report

(10 points) Clarity _____ Comments _____

_____

_____

(20 points) Accuracy _____ Comments _____

_____

_____

(10 points) Timeliness _____ Comments _____

_____

_____

(10 points) Neatness _____ Comments _____

_____

_____

TOTAL POINTS _____

Design and Costs of Rooms Report

Your group is now ready to design your individual rooms and calculate the expenses for constructing, painting, and furnishing your teen center.

Materials

The **engineer** needs to get the following:

- Several pieces of $\frac{1}{4}$-inch graph paper
- Two or three rulers
- Store catalogs
- Graphing calculator
- Sharp pencils
- Construction paper for cutouts
- Felt-tip black pen
- Yardstick or tape measure

The **statistician** is responsible for making sure that group members obtain the following information:

- Maximum capacity for your teen center based on the square footage of the center (Unit 1)
- Number of stalls or urinals in each restroom needed based on your maximum capacity. Also, how many handicapped stalls are necessary in each restroom?
- Dimensions of bathroom stalls (including handicapped) and urinals

Building a Teen Center
©1998 Key Curriculum Press

Design and Costs of Rooms Report

- Height and width of the walls (you should already have width in your blueprint)
- Slant degree for handicapped ramps mandated by zoning ordinances in your community
- Dimensions for dishwasher, stove, refrigerator, ice maker, and so on, if you have a kitchen
- Number of seats necessary in your establishment based on your maximum capacity

The **recorder** is responsible for making sure that the following is included in the typed report.

Design

- Design of each room, including everything in the room, on a sheet of graph paper

Items

- List of the physical items (tables, desks, chairs, and so on) in each room
- List of the choices of paint or wallpaper and tile or carpet

Costs

- List of the costs of each physical item, paint or wallpaper, and tile or carpet in each room
- List of the total interior costs (use matrices)
- List of the construction costs for building the structure
- List of the exterior costs (painting)
- A total of all the costs for furnishing, painting, carpeting, and building the teen center

The **project leader** is responsible for making sure that everyone is on task and will meet the timeline.

Projected Expenses per Month

Numbers are to a mathematician what bags of coins are to an investment banker; nominally the stuff of his profession, but actually too gritty and particular to waste time on. Ideas are the real currency of mathematicians.

—James Gleick, *Chaos: Making a New Science*, 1987.

This unit requires that students combine the information in Units 1 and 3 with information they will obtain in Unit 4. They will do a little research on their food and drink inventory, which involves adding, multiplying, and constructing a pie chart and a bar graph. This is an excellent opportunity to show your students how to use a computer spreadsheet program. My students learned to do a pie chart and bar graph by hand first, but for the project they used a computer.

This unit of the project demonstrates the fact that when we use mathematics in the real world, it does not follow the order of our curriculum. Unit 4 has simplistic mathematics, whereas the earlier units had more complex mathematics. For their teen center, each group will construct spreadsheets, pie charts, and bar graphs for their nightly food and drink inventory, cost of their labor, costs for the construction of their building and interior (Unit 3), and finally their projected monthly expenses, which includes their monthly loan payment, personnel costs, and utilities (Unit 1). It is difficult to include all the costs necessary for a business to stay open, so the costs of many items will not be included in this unit.

Mathematical Concepts

- Using a pie chart to represent data
- Using a bar graph to represent data
- Using technology (computers and calculators)

Lessons

- 4-1: Spreadsheets, Pie Charts, and Bar Graphs
- 4-2: Projected Expenses for the Teen Center

Assessment

Each of the activities has a built-in assessment. Home Activity 4-1: Grocery Shopping will demonstrate each student's understanding of how to create a spreadsheet, a pie chart, and a bar graph by hand. Also, as an integral part of the teen center, each group member has to generate (hopefully by computer) his or her individual part of the final report for Group Activity 4-2: Teen Center's Projected Expenses per Month.

Extension

Taxes, payroll, and social security can be introduced and discussed. Since most teenagers work at some point when attending high school, students might find such a discussion very valuable. This also provides a wonderful opportunity to invite to class a small-business owner who could talk about set-up costs and profit/expense ratios.

Spreadsheets, Pie Charts, and Bar Graphs

This lesson can be done either with paper and pencil or by using a computer spreadsheet program. I worked through the lesson with my students because I found that they had minimal experience working with organizing data and that even my Algebra I honors students had little experience with pie charts and bar graphs.

Objective

- To help students develop the ability to carry out numerical calculations effectively, to create and interpret a pie graph and bar graph by hand and/or with technology

Materials

- Protractors
- Calculators
- Computer with spreadsheet program (optional)

Resources

- Individual Activity 4-1: Teen Center's Nightly Food and Drink Inventory
- Transparency 4-1a: Sample Spreadsheet
- Transparency 4-1b: Sample Pie Chart and Bar Graph
- Home Activity 4-1: Grocery Shopping

Class Activity 4-1
Teen Center's Food and Drink Inventory   60 minutes

For this activity, you may use Individual Activity 4-1 as a transparency so that the students can follow along. It provides the opportunity for the students to organize their data into a spreadsheet and then construct a pie chart and bar graph. This activity simulates what each group will do when they set up their own food and drink inventory for their own teen center.

Home Activity 4-1
Grocery Shopping

This activity focuses on getting prices for various food and drink items. The students can either go to the grocery store or use the food ads in the newspaper. For my students who did not receive a newspaper, I provided a number of food sections from newspapers for them to take home. If you want your students to go to a grocery store, then allow more than one night for the assignment. However, if they are using newspaper ads, one night should be sufficient.

Teen Center's Nightly Food and Drink Inventory

The following list contains food and drink items that your teen center might serve to your customers in one evening. On a separate sheet of paper or on a computer spreadsheet program, take the list of items and prices and organize them into edibles, nonedibles, and drinks. The list shows 1997 prices, before tax, and reflects planning for approximately 50 customers.

Supplies for One Evening

Item	Quantity	Price
Fried chicken (8 pieces per bucket)	12 buckets	$59.88
Three-bean salad ($2.39 per pound)	5 pounds	$11.95
Potato salad ($1.89 per pound)	5 pounds	$ 9.45
Pasta salad ($3.29 per pound)	5 pounds	$16.45
Cole slaw ($2.49 per pound)	5 pounds	$12.45
Napkins (from recycled paper, 250 per package)	1 package	$ 1.79
Assorted plastic utensils (24 per box)	5 boxes	$ 5.45
Apples (88¢ per pound)	5 pounds	$ 4.40
Oranges (99¢ per pound)	5 pounds	$ 4.95
Apple juice ($2.99 per gallon)	2 gallons	$ 5.98
Milk (36¢ per half pint)	30 half pints	$10.80
9-ounce paper cups (80 per package)	1 package	$ 2.79
Paper plates (150 per package)	1 package	$ 3.85

Teen Center's Nightly Food and Drink Inventory

Setting Up the Spreadsheet

Take the preceding data and organize your items:

1. Use three separate headings: Edibles, Nonedibles, and Drinks.
2. Make separate columns for Item, How Many, Price Per Item, and Total Cost Per Item.
3. Leave space at the end of edibles, nonedibles, and drinks for the total cost of each type of item.

Your spreadsheet should show the following information.

- The **total cost** of the items in each category: edibles, nonedibles, and drinks
- The total cost of all items used in an evening

4. On a separate sheet of paper or using a computer spreadsheet program, draw a pie chart that shows the percentage of the cost of edibles, nonedibles, and drinks for each night.
5. Take the same information and construct a bar graph. Label your *y*-axis as Cost and set your scale at increments of $100. For the *x*-axis, label each bar as Edibles, Nonedibles, and Drinks. Make sure your bar graph has a title.

Sample Spreadsheet

Teen Center's Food and Drink Inventory Per Evening

Item	Quantity	Price per item	Total cost
Edibles			
Fried chicken (8 pieces per bucket)	12	$4.99	$59.88
		Total cost	
Nonedibles			
Napkins	4	$2.50	$10.00
		Total cost	
Drinks			
		Total cost	
Inventory	Cost		
Edibles			
Nonedibles			
Drinks			
Total cost per evening			

Building a Teen Center
©1998 Key Curriculum Press

Sample Pie Chart and Bar Graph

Pie Chart

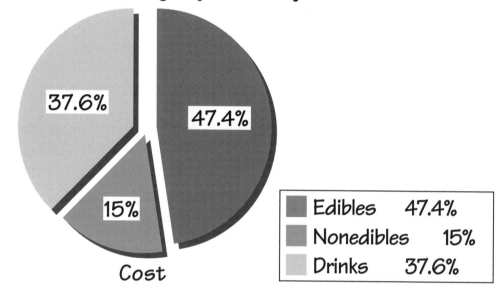

Food and Drink Nightly Inventory

■	Edibles	47.4%
■	Nonedibles	15%
■	Drinks	37.6%

Bar Graph

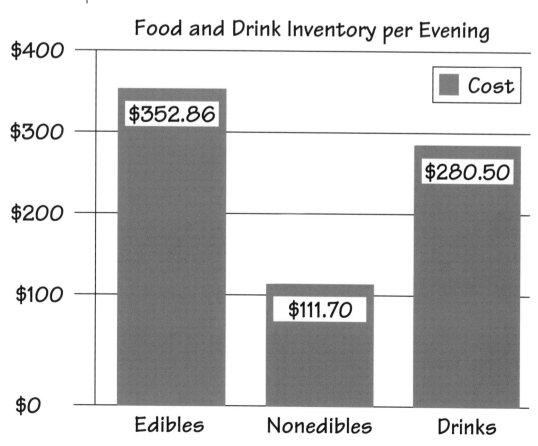

Food and Drink Inventory per Evening

Grocery Shopping

Use your own paper when completing this activity.

1. Take the food section out of any newspaper and find at least seven edible items, five nonedible items, three kinds of soft drinks, and two different kinds of juice. (When you turn in the assignment, include the newspaper ads you used.)

2. Construct a spreadsheet that lists the item, how many you are going to buy of that item, price per item, and total cost of the item. Classify your items into edibles, nonedibles, and drinks. The spreadsheet you are creating is like the one you did in class. Make sure you include a total cost for your grocery list at the end.

3. Construct a pie chart by using a protractor. Show all of your computations.

4. Using the same information, construct a bar graph.

5. Compare your shopping list with one that your parent(s) or another adult has used recently. How much money did you spend? How much money did they spend? Are you surprised? Why or why not?

Projected Expenses for the Teen Center

This lesson focuses on each group's ability to calculate their projected expenses per month. Each group member is required to contribute a spreadsheet, and the members need to work together in order to achieve the final result. This part of the project demonstrates the need for individual diversification. Four different spreadsheets need to be prepared: Nightly Food and Drink Inventory, Cost of Personnel, Construction of the Building and Exterior and Interior Costs, and Projected Expenses per Month. Each member of the group is responsible for a separate spreadsheet.

Objective
- To help students use a computer to develop a spreadsheet, pie chart, and bar graph

Materials
- Computer with a spreadsheet program (optional)
- Several food sections from newspapers
- Preliminary Information Sheet (Unit 1)
- Design and Costs Rooms Report (Units 3–6)

Resource
- Group Activity 4-2: Teen Center's Projected Expenses per Month

 Group Activity 4-2
Teen Center's Projected Expenses per Month   3 to 4 hours

Each member of the teen center groups will be required to contribute individually to the entire report. However, before students sit down at the computer and do their individual spreadsheets, they must do some preliminary work on their nightly food and drink inventory. Students should determine what they want to serve in their establishment, find out how much food they will need based on their maximum capacity, and then calculate food costs from the food section of the newspaper. Also, each group must calculate how many hours a day they want their teen center to stay open; how many employees they need (including themselves); and how many hours the employees need to work. The groups must be aware that there has to be set-up time, after-hours work, and office time for keeping the books, ordering, and handling other administrative details. They will need advice on certain aspects on running a business.

Each group should determine all of their expenses, such as food and drink inventory for six months, constructions costs, and interior and exterior costs for painting, carpeting/tiling, and furnishings. This is the amount of money they will have to borrow from the bank. Although the process of obtaining a business loan is not covered until Unit 7, the students do have to have a monthly payment now. It is easy to get repayment schedules from the banks for students to use. The price tag will be high—some of my students had loans in the million-dollar range.

I have not included any specific home activities, because the groups will have to meet time limits and some of their research work for their particular spreadsheet can be done at home.

Teen Center's Projected Expenses per Month

Each group member is responsible for one part.

Part I: Nightly Food and Drink Inventory

Group Member Responsible _____

To organize this part of the project, you need to answer and complete the following, using your own paper:

1. What is the maximum capacity of your teen center? (Refer to Unit 1.)
2. Make up a preliminary menu of what you want to serve your customers.
3. List edibles, nonedibles, and drinks that you need for your establishment. Then find the price per item from the food sections of newspapers. Cut out the food section(s) you used and neatly glue them onto unlined paper.
4. Create a Nightly Food and Drink Inventory spreadsheet on a computer. For your report, turn in a spreadsheet with only formulas showing (no graphs), a spreadsheet with actual numbers and a pie chart, and a spreadsheet with actual numbers and a bar graph.
5. Multiply the total cost of the Nightly Food and Drink Inventory by the number of nights your club is going to be open in a month. Then multiply that cost by 6 months. This is how much money your club must have in order to feed your customers for a 6-month period. (To find how many days your club is open in a month, talk to the group member responsible for the Personnel spreadsheet.)

Teen Center's Projected Expenses per Month

Part II: Personnel

Group Member Responsible _____

To organize this part of the project, you need to answer and complete the following questions, using your own paper:

1. How many hours will your teen center be open per day? What are the hours?

2. How many days will your teen center be open per month?

3. What days of the week will your teen center *not* be open?

4. Make a list of the types of employees you will need. (Remember, you need someone to cook, clean, wait tables, watch the video room, possibly someone to sing or play CDs, keep the books, pay the employees, and in general oversee the entire operation.)

5. Based on your number of tables, how many servers will you assign to the floor? Show your work on how you figured this out.

6. Develop a spreadsheet based on job description, hourly wage, how many hours worked, and total wages paid *for each type of job*. Include a spreadsheet with formulas only, a spreadsheet with actual numbers and a pie chart, and a spreadsheet with actual numbers and a bar graph.

7. Multiply the total wages paid per evening by the number of days per month that your teen center is open.

Teen Center's Projected Expenses per Month

Part III: Building Costs

Group Member Responsible _____

To organize this part of the project, you need to answer and complete the following:

Refer to Unit 3 to develop your spreadsheet.

1. Develop a spreadsheet based on construction costs of the building, painting (exterior and interior), carpeting/tiling, and furnishings (list by room and items going into each room).

2. Produce three different spreadsheets: a spreadsheet with formulas only, a spreadsheet with actual numbers and a pie chart, and a spreadsheet with actual numbers and a bar graph.

3. What are the total costs of building, painting, and furnishing?

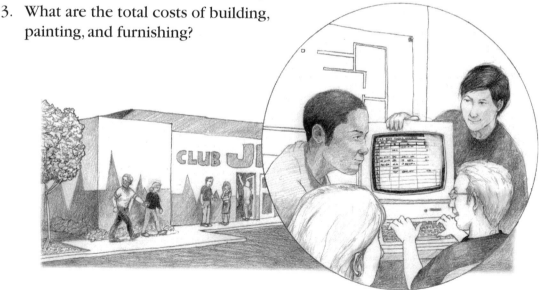

Teen Center's Projected Expenses per Month

Part IV: Projected Expenses Per Month

Group Member Responsible _____

To organize this part of the project, you need to answer and complete the following:

Check with your other group members to complete your spreadsheet.

1. Nightly Food and Drink Inventory for 6 months _____

    + Building Costs _____

    Total Amount of Loan Needed: _____

2. Monthly payment on a 30-year loan (check with your teacher for loan payments): _____

3. Develop a spreadsheet that includes monthly loan payment, personnel costs per month, and cost of utilities per month (Unit 1). List the different utilities and their costs.

4. Produce three different spreadsheets: a spreadsheet with formulas only, a spreadsheet with actual numbers and a pie chart, and a spreadsheet with actual numbers and a bar graph.

5. What will be your teen center's projected monthly expenses?

6. Divide your monthly expenses by the number of days your center is open per month and figure out what your expenses are for one day.

7. Write a paragraph representing the views of your entire group. Was your group surprised at how much money is needed to keep your center open for a month? A day? Do you think your center will be able to generate enough money to stay open and be successful?

Making a Profit

Present-day high school algebra experiences are like the experiences of a Little Leaguer who practices catching and hitting but never plays the game.

—NCTM, *Algebra in a Technological World*, 1995

This unit gives the students an opportunity to think about how their teen center is going to generate money. They will create menus, establish prices, and decide whether or not a cover charge is feasible. Mathematically, students will use linear equations to visualize cost, revenue, and profit. By applying this difficult topic to the development of the teen center, students should have a better understanding of linear equations than they would with ordinary pencil-and-paper manipulation.

Linear equations is a topic that is extensively reviewed every year as students move up the ladder to higher-level mathematics courses. One excellent way to approach this subject is to use a project that has students look at patterns, think about which variables and constants are important, make a table, graph the ordered pairs, and then fit points to an equation. Since a project helps to contextualize the mathematics, this approach gives students a more thorough understanding of why it is necessary to write equations. A graphing calculator or a computer is a tool they can use to immediately see whether or not their equation is correct. If the graph of the equation goes through their data, then each student knows he or she has been successful. The use of technology eliminates the need to solve a problem by just guessing or by using repetitive arithmetic skills. When my students have a reason to solve equations, they are more willing to learn all the rules and properties that are necessary in algebra.

Mathematical Concepts

- Graphing linear equations
- Using the graphing capabilities of a calculator
- Interpreting slope in a real situation
- Determining the intuitive notion of domain and range of a linear function
- Using various features of a graph to answer questions about a situation
- Discussing limitations of a mathematical model
- Interpreting information from a graph

Lessons

- 5-1: The Cartesian Coordinate System
- 5-2: Developing an Equation
- 5-3: Slope and y-Intercept
- 5-4: Designing the Logo and Menu
- 5-5: Making a Profit

Assessment

Individual Activity 5-3: Selling T-Shirts can be used as an assessment activity to evaluate whether the students understand slope, y-intercept, patterns, developing an equation, and using that equation to predict from their equation. Also, it reveals their understanding of the graphing calculator and the informal notion of domain and range. It also introduces words that are important to the concept of their teen center: cost, revenue, and profit.

Individual Assessment 5-5: A Graphic Investigation is a formal assessment tool to help determine each student's understanding of linear equations.

The Cartesian Coordinate System

This lesson introduces the Cartesian coordinate system and how to use it to plot points. The lesson is not intended to give a complete and in-depth exposure to graphing, but rather to provide students with the basics so that they can produce the equations and graphs that are necessary to look at some profit structures for their teen center. Even if you are not doing the teen center project, the activities in this lesson will reinforce understanding of graphing and equations.

Objective
- To have students use graphs to explore patterns of numbers, as well as data, and to introduce the cartesian coordinate system

Materials
- Graph paper $\left(\frac{1}{4} \text{ inch grid}\right)$
- Ruler or straight edge

Resources
- Transparency 5-1: Cartesian Coordinate System
- Partner Activity 5-1: Graphing Data on a Coordinate Plane
- Home Activity 5-1: Help Wanted

Class Activity 5-1
Introduction of Cartesian Coordinate System   20 minutes

Open the lesson with a formal explanation of the Cartesian coordinate system, who created the system, and why. Transparency 5-1 introduces the Cartesian plane and shows the various parts of the system.

Partner Activity 5-1
Graphing Data on a Coordinate Plane   30 minutes

This activity gives students some practice plotting points and connecting them to see a predictable pattern.

Home Activity 5-1
Help Wanted

This activity is an adaptation of a problem in NCTM's *Algebra in a Technological World*. Students have the opportunity to work with data and tables, from which they can create ordered pairs and plot them on their graph. Since these are linear equations, this activity is a good opening for the lesson on slope and *y*-intercept. The activity is rather open-ended, and it is interesting to see the students' results. The biggest confusion will be the $150 and what to do with it.

Cartesian Coordinate System

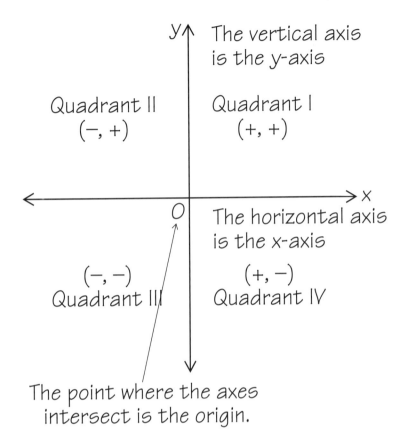

The Cartesian coordinate system is named after a French mathematician, René Descartes (1596–1650).

The two **axes** (*x*-axis and *y*-axis) of this system are perpendicular (form right angles) and divide the coordinate plane into four **quadrants** labeled counterclockwise I, II, III, and IV.

Every point in the plane can be described by an ordered pair of values— the **coordinates** of the point.

A (2, 3.5)   B (−5, 4)

C (−2, 0)   D (2, −3.5)

E (−4, −3)   F (0, 4)

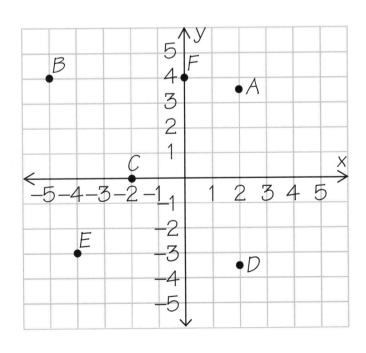

Graphing Data on a Coordinate Plane

1. Explain how the points $(3, 5)$ and $(5, 3)$ are different.

2. Match the term on the left with the phrase on the right that best describes it.

   a. coordinate plane

   b. abscissa

   c. perpendicular
   d. *x*-axis
   e. *y*-axis
   f. coordinates

   g. origin

   i. intersecting lines that form right angles
   ii. system used in math for graphing pairs of numbers
   iii. horizontal axis
   iv. vertical axis
   v. point of intersection of axes
   vi. ordered pairs of numbers assigned to a point
   vii. first number in ordered pair

3. The coordinates of S are $(1, -4)$.

   a. What is the *x*-coordinate of point S?
   b. What is the *y*-coordinate of point S?

On a separate sheet of graph paper or on your graphing calculator, graph the following:

4. Plot the points $(-1, -1), (1, 2), (3, 5), (5, 8), (7, 11)$. Connect the points. What did you draw when you connected the points?

5. Plot the points $(-3, 9), (-2, 4), (-1, 1), (0, 0), (1, 1), (2, 4), (3, 9)$. Connect the points. What kind of shape do the connected points form?

6. The graph below shows the position of four soccer players. What are the coordinates of Players *A*, *B*, *C*, and *D*?

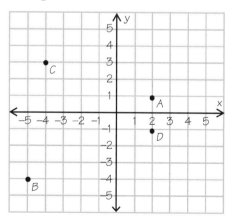

Help Wanted

Your 12-week summer vacation is about to begin and you have two
job offers:

- Joline's Construction Company, which won't be open the first
  two weeks of vacation. The job guarantees you $9 an hour and
  a 40-hour week.
- Joe's Wreck & Build, which can pay you only $6.25 an hour and
  guarantees a 40-hour week. In addition, Joe's offers you a bonus of
  $175, payable at the end of the 12 weeks, if you start immediately.

Do you think you would make more money at Joline's Construction
Company or Joe's Wreck & Build? Do the problems below.

1. Make a table representing 12 weeks and how much money you would
   make per week.

2. Graph your results on graph paper. Use the tables to create the ordered
   pairs. Use two different colored pencils, one for Joline's and one for
   Joe's. You are to determine which information will represent the *x*-axis
   and which information will represent the *y*-axis. You will also need to
   determine how to set up your scale.

Developing an Equation

The purpose of this lesson is for the students to develop an intuitive notion of slope and y-intercept. This is accomplished with the use of patterns, tables, and graphs. After students have had sufficient practice, formal definitions of slope and y-intercept are introduced in Lesson 5-3.

Objectives
- To have students recognize the relationship between an equation of a line and the coordinates of points on that line
- To have students develop intuitive notions about the general locations of graphs in the forms $y = ax$ and $y = ax + b$

Materials
- Graph paper $\left(\frac{1}{4}\text{ inch grid}\right)$
- Graphing calculator

Resources
- Group Activity 5-2: Wasting Water
- Home Activity 5-2: Buying Towels

Class Activity 5-2
Review of Home Activity 5-1   20 minutes

Your students will have done Home Activity 5-1 in a variety of ways and probably will not have answered the questions completely. You can use this as an opportunity to set up a table, look for a pattern, graph the pattern, and then, through a discussion of slope and y-intercept, develop an equation.

Group Activity 5-2
Wasting Water   20 minutes

This activity will continue the development of the equation process and intuitively finding the y-intercept, and slope.

Home Activity 5-2
Buying Towels

This problem is open-ended, but it gives students one more opportunity to develop a table, discover a pattern, plot their data points, write a rule (equation), and then use their rule (equation) to answer questions. A graphing calculator is needed to answer a few of the questions in this activity. These questions can be eliminated if the students do not have graphing calculators available.

Wasting Water

Club Wisdom has a leaky shower in the girl's locker room and Andrea, the manager, is alarmed to learn that 3 gallons of water is being wasted per minute. The table below shows the relationship between m, the number of minutes the faucet runs, and g, the number of gallons wasted.

m	1	2	3	4	5	6
g	3	6				

1. Finish the table and then plot the above data points (m, g). Connect your data points.
2. Use the graph to estimate the amount of water wasted in 7 minutes.
3. Write a rule that tells how to find the number of gallons wasted when you know the number of minutes the faucet runs.
4. Enter the minutes in L1 and the gallons wasted in L2. Turn on Stat Plot 1, define your Window and then press Graph. Describe your STAT PLOT and your WINDOW on paper.
5. Use your rule to estimate the number of gallons wasted when the faucet has been running 20 minutes.
6. Enter your equation in the $Y =$ menu. Does the graph of the equation you created contain all the data points?

Buying Towels

Andrea, Club Wisdom's manager, needs to buy towels for the locker rooms. She sees the ad shown at right.

1. Create a table that shows the cost of ordering from 1 to 6 towels.

2. Using your graphing calculator or a separate sheet of graph paper, graph the ordered pairs from the table you created.

3. Using your pattern, write an equation for the cost of the towels where x represents the number of towels purchased and y represents the price.

4. Graph the equation to check to see if it goes through the ordered pairs.

5. Use your equation to calculate the following: How much would 150 towels cost? 200 towels? Show on paper how you used your equation.

COTTON TOWEL SALE

Only $6.00 a towel

TOP QUALITY

Call 1-800-555-4444

(Add $6.50 for shipping)

Slope and y-Intercept

In this lesson, students are given only two points to find the equation of a line. At this time you can formally introduce them to slope and y-intercept. Informally, in Lesson 5-2, they wrote their equations in slope-intercept form, $y = mx + b$. Now, they are ready to give it a formal name. It will probably take two hours to do this entire lesson.

Objectives

- To have students determine the equation of a line through two given points
- To have students write their equations in slope-intercept form, $y = mx + b$
- To have students apply and interpret a graphical solution to a system of equations

Materials

- Graph paper $\left(\frac{1}{4} \text{ inch grid}\right)$
- Graphing calculator (optional)

Resources

- Group Activity 5-3: French Fries
- Individual Activity 5-3: Selling T-shirts

 Class Activity 5-3
Review of Home Activity 5-2   *20 minutes*

If your students have access to their graphing calculator only in school, allow them about 10 minutes to enter their data and see if their equation works. Use this time to go around the room to see who has and who has not done their assignment.

Use this as an opportunity to formally introduce the terms **slope** and **intercept** and introduce the general form of the linear equation $y = mx + b$. After checking to see if the students' assignments are complete, choose two points on their line and use the formula $m = \frac{y_1 - y_2}{x_1 - x_2}$ to derive the slope of the line.

Because your students informally found the slope during the assignment, they may see that the number that preceded x was the slope. Use $y = mx + b$ to derive b and the y-intercept. In this problem, the y-intercept has a real-world meaning. It represents the delivery cost.

I often return to activities that my students have previously done. Because the students are familiar with the problems, it is easier to show that a different approach will result in the same answer.

Once students have a grasp of the material, introduce them to the terms **domain** and **range**. I always begin my discussion of domain and range without using those two words. However, in order to see their data, students have to be able to create a window that will show them their data. Then when I formally introduce those two words, I find it an easy transition to get them to use their calculator window.

Group Activity 5-3
French Fries   45 minutes

This activity gets quite involved, because the students create two equations, much like they did in Home Activity 5-1: Help Wanted. They examine two different lines to make predictions. In this case, they determine which company Roberta should go with when she is ordering a large quantity of french fries. This activity is also an informal introduction to systems of equations that the students can solve graphically using their graphing calculator.

Individual Activity 5-3
Selling T-Shirts   60 minutes

This activity can be done at home or in groups during class time or it could be used as a form of assessment. The activity also introduces the concept of inequalities because the students need to think about more than a single number as a solution. The activity allows them to become aware of key concepts such as cost, revenue, and profit that are important to the management and operation of their teen centers. The activity also further strengthens their development of equations, slope and y-intercept, domain and range, and overall graphing skills.

French Fries

One of the New Dimension Teen Center's most popular food items is french fries. Roberta, the new manager, has noticed that there are two different food outlets that sell good-quality french fries, and she has to make a choice between the two. Roberta asks that Yvonne's Food Outlet and Clarence's Specialty Outlet send her their cost proposals for french fries.

    Yvonne's sells 5-pound bags of french fries for $7.50 per bag and has a $10.00 delivery charge. Clarence's sells 5-pound bags for $7.00 per bag and has an $18.00 delivery charge. Roberta needs to decide which food outlet to use. One outlet is cheaper per bag but has a more expensive delivery charge, whereas the other has a lower delivery charge but is more expensive per bag. She recalls her high school algebra course and decides to use what she remembers about linear equations to help her decide which food outlet to use. Put yourself in Roberta's shoes and answer the following questions.

1. First, Roberta constructs two tables: one for Yvonne's and the other for Clarence's.

<table>
<tr><th colspan="4">Yvonne's Food Outlet</th></tr>
<tr><th>No. of bags</th><th>Price</th><th>Delivery</th><th>Total</th></tr>
<tr><td>1</td><td>$7.50</td><td>$10.00</td><td>$17.50</td></tr>
<tr><td></td><td></td><td></td><td></td></tr>
</table>

<table>
<tr><th colspan="4">Clarence's Specialty Outlet</th></tr>
<tr><th>No. of bags</th><th>Price</th><th>Delivery</th><th>Total</th></tr>
<tr><td>1</td><td>$7.00</td><td>$18.00</td><td>$25.00</td></tr>
<tr><td></td><td></td><td></td><td></td></tr>
</table>

Roberta enters the tables into her graphing calculator and realizes that there is a relationship between the number of bags purchased and the cost of the french fries. Roberta tires of making a table because she sometimes orders 50 bags per week, so she feels an equation would be easier to use and she realizes that there is a pattern.

2. A quantity that varies in a situation is called a **variable**. What are the two quantities that are varying in Roberta's situation?

3. A quantity that remains the same is called a **constant**. There are two constants in her situation. What are they?

4. As Roberta went from 1 bag to 2 bags, 2 bags to 3 bags, 3 bags to 4 bags, and so on, she noticed that she was adding the same number each time. For Yvonne's Food Outlet, what was that number? What was it for Clarence's Specialty Outlet?

French Fries

5. From high school algebra, Roberta remembered the formula $m = \frac{y_1 - y_2}{x_1 - x_2}$, and she feels that somehow she could use it here. Can you help Roberta out by telling her what the formula would tell her?

6. If Roberta did not buy any bags of french fries (which would be quite silly), but had the truck make a delivery anyway, what would the delivery costs be for both food outlets? She thought of this silly idea because, again, she remembered her high school algebra. The thought came into her head that if x were equal to zero, then y would equal the delivery cost. What exactly was she remembering?

7. Roberta felt that she was ready to write her equations, one for Yvonne's and one for Clarence's. If you are ready, write the two equations. Then use them to find out which company would be cheaper to use if Roberta were ordering her 50 bags for the week.

8. Sometimes, Roberta runs out of fries and needs just 15 or 20 bags. Would it still be cheaper to use the food outlet that she chose for the 50 bags? Justify your answer and explain using a table or graph, why or why not. At how many bags do both food outlets charge the same amount of money?

Selling T-Shirts

Roberta, the manager of the New Dimension Teen Center, decides that to help promote their business and increase their advertising they will make their own T-shirts and sell them. To get the mini-business started, she finds out that the start-up cost will be $200 and it will cost an additional $3 to produce each T-shirt. The New Dimension Teen Center plans to sell the T-shirts for $7.50 each. As Roberta's assistant, you are going to do the mathematics for her.

Part I: Cost

Answer the questions below on a separate sheet of paper. If you are using a graphing calculator, sketch each graph and write down your window settings.

1. Make a table with two columns that shows the cost of producing 1, 2, 3, 4, and 5 T-shirts. Plot the data points from your table.
2. a. Remember, the equation to find the slope is $m = \frac{y_1 - y_2}{x_1 - x_2}$. Select two ordered pairs from your table and find the slope.
   b. What does the slope in this equation correspond to?
3. Write an equation in slope-intercept form ($y = mx + b$) describing the relationship between the number of T-shirts and the cost of the T-shirts.
4. What is your y-intercept? What is the real-world meaning of the y-intercept?
5. Why do you think it is important to write an equation?
6. What will the equation allow you to do?
7. Graph your equation on your calculator or on paper. Does your graph go through the data points? If it does, congratulations, you have the correct equation. If it does not, check your work and find an equation that does go through your points.
8. Now, use your equation to find out how much it would cost to produce 100 T-shirts, 150 T-shirts, and 450 T-shirts.

Building a Teen Center
©1998 Key Curriculum Press

Selling T-Shirts

Part II: Revenue

Now that you have found out the **cost** of producing the T-shirts, you need to find out how much money the teen center will make from the sale of the T-shirts. This is called **revenue**. Use your graphing calculator or a separate sheet of graph paper to answer the questions below.

1. Each T-shirt sells for $7.50. Make a chart showing the revenue generated by selling 1, 2, 3, 4, and 5 T-shirts.
2. Graph your ordered pairs comparing the *number of T-shirts* and the *revenue*.
3. Draw a line connecting the points and find the slope. What would be the real-world meaning of the revenue slope?
4. What is your *y*-intercept? What is the real-world meaning of the revenue *y*-intercept?
5. Write an equation in slope-intercept form ($y = mx + b$) describing the relationship between the number of T-shirts and the revenue from selling the T-shirts.
6. Graph your equation. Does it go through the data points? If it does, congratulations, you have the correct equation. If it does not, change your equation until you have one that fits your points.
7. Now, use your equation to find out how much revenue is produced by selling 40 T-shirts, 100 T-shirts, 150 T-shirts, and 450 T-shirts.
8. If you have a graphing calculator available, use it to find the revenue produced by selling 100, 150, and 450 T-shirts. Did you get the same answer as you did when you solved the equation algebraically? If you did, again congratulations, you did your algebra correctly.

Selling T-Shirts

Part III: Profit

1. Profit occurs after the break-even point. What do you think is meant by the break-even point?

2. Create a chart like the one below that shows the cost, revenue, and net profit or loss for selling a given number of T-shirts. Use your equations or graphing calculator to help you find your answers.

Number of T-shirts	Cost	Revenue	Net profit or loss
1			
5			
10			
20			
30			
35			
40			
45			
50			

3. From your table, approximately where do you think the break-even point is?

4. From the graphs on your graphing calculator, describe where you think the break-even point is.

5. Using your revenue equation, write an inequality that would represent when the teen center would be making a profit on their T-shirts.

6. If the teen center wants to make a profit of $2,000 from their T-shirt sales, how many T-shirts do they need to sell?

This lesson is an extension of the T-shirt idea and one in which the students can actually make the T-shirts by hand or do programs on the computer. Doing the T-shirts by hand is fun and the students really enjoy it. The menu not only gives them an opportunity to get more computer experience, but it also is important for the next lesson, in which they will develop equations for their own break-even point. This lesson is a departure from the mathematics, but it still is worthwhile in that students are working together to come up with a common product and it *can* give more opportunities to work with computers.

Objectives

- To give students the opportunity to work cooperatively to come up with a common product
- To give students the opportunity to use graphics on a computer

Materials

- Business typing paper (25% cotton)
- Iron and ironing board
- Computers with a graphic program
- Plain white paper
- Fabric crayons (preferably Crayola®)
- Plain white T-shirts that are 100% cotton

Resource

- Group Activity 5-4: Creating Your Logo and Menu

 **Group Activity 5-4**
Creating Your Logo and Menu   75 minutes

I have written this activity so that two members of each group are working on the logo and the other two members are working on the menu. However, if you choose to do the logo and menu at different times, that is fine.

Prior to doing this part of the project, ask students to purchase an all-white T-shirt that is 100% cotton. You can also purchase a number of T-shirts from various outlets for as little as $2 a T-shirt. For the T-shirt, ask the students to design a logo on plain white paper or tracing paper and then, when they are satisfied, to draw the logo on the business paper and color it with the fabric crayons. (I have found from personal experience that Crayola works the best.) **Remind them that any writing will have to be done backward in order for it to appear correctly on the T-shirt.** Have the students center the logo on the T-shirt where they want the logo to appear. My students used light pencil marks. Then take a very hot iron, no steam, and place a plain white sheet of paper on the ironing board, drape the T-shirt over the board, line up the logo face down with the pencil marks, and place another white sheet of paper on top, and iron. Keep the iron moving and do it for a few minutes. I found that for the first few I did I had not gone over the paper enough. Go over and over the edges and try to keep the paper from sliding. Take the paper off and there should be the logo.

Here is a simple version of a sample menu. With your students' menu, check to see that they have listed realistic prices. A lot of my students had worked in fast-food restaurants or had eaten out enough to be fairly realistic. However, I did have students that were way off on their pricing. Some of my groups were very creative, and others had very plain-looking menus. I also had my students do preliminary sketches by hand before they went on the computer. Two groups preferred doing their menu by hand instead of using the computer, and I did not force the issue. I let it be their choice.

Menu

Fried chicken	$1.25
Pasta salad	$1.25
Three-bean salad	$ .55
Potato salad	$ .55
Cole slaw	$ .55

Snacks

Apples	$ .50
Oranges	$ .50

Drinks

Apple juice	$ .55
Milk	$ .55

Creating Your Logo and Menu

In order for any business to make a profit, the public must be aware of its existence, so two of you are going to design a logo and make T-shirts for your teen center. The other two are going to design a menu for your establishment. Therefore, two of you are going to do Part I and the other two are going to do Part II. Since this is a group project and you are dividing your labor, check with each other as you are doing your part or as you finish your part. The other half of your group may have some helpful suggestions to make your logo or menu even better.

Part I: Creating Your Logo

1. Take some plain white paper or tracing paper and design your logo. Any writing will have to be done backward in order for it to appear correctly when it is transferred to the T-shirt.

2. Transfer your logo to the business typing paper that is 25% cotton. This paper must be used in order for your logo to come out on your T-shirt.

3. Now, using the fabric crayons, color your logo and write your words. Do not color too lightly or too hard. If the coloring is too light, it will not come through and if it is too hard, it will smear.

4. When you are finished, bring the logo to your teacher and she or he will iron it on to your T-shirts.

Part II: Creating the Menu

1. On a plain white piece of paper, sketch and write out your menu. Remember, your teen center would like to make a profit, but keep your prices reasonable.

2. When you are ready, use the graphic part of the program you have been using to create pictures or use pictures from a scrapbook.

3. If you have a color printer, you could do your menu in color.

Now is the time for the groups to establish how they are going to make some money to keep their teen centers in the black. For the group activity, they use their work from Unit 4. I have also included an individual assessment that is performance based. It revolves around the concept of the teen center but gives you the opportunity to see if each student understands the concept of linear equations.

Objectives

- To have students apply and determine the graphical solution to systems of equations
- To have students write their equations in slope-intercept form, $y = mx + b$

Materials

- Graphing calculator (optional)
- Graph paper $\left(\frac{1}{4} \text{ inch grid}\right)$

Resources

- Group Activity 5-5: Making a Profit for Your Teen Center
- Individual Assessment 5-5: A Graphic Investigation

 **Group Activity 5-5**
Making a Profit   *90 minutes*

This activity is one of the unit's culminating activities. Using the figure they calculated in Unit 4 for the expenses per month, the groups determine their expenses per evening. Next, they estimate how much each customer will spend per evening and make a linear graph based on their predictions.

To estimate the amount of money they expect per customer, the students should use their menu. For example, they can choose three items from their menu such as a hamburger, french fries, and a juice, and then determine the total price for those three items. This is the figure they will use as their price per customer per evening. In this activity, students will have to think about such things as whether there is enough inventory to serve the customers' needs. This will require that they look at their bulk food items and break them down into individual servings.

In the second half of this activity, students can add a third color to indicate their profit structure if they add a cover charge.

The individual assessment has been adapted from a Bob Davis activity, "Mr. Teeny Bop's Night Club—A Graphic Investigation." The assessment provides an opportunity to see if students understand the relationship between a graph of a simple linear equation and the equation itself. Also, an intuitive understanding of slope and intercepts is fostered.

Making a Profit for Your Teen Center

In order for your establishment to receive a loan to build your building and establish credit, your group has to show the financial institution how you are going to generate money. Is your teen center a good financial risk?

Part I: Price Structure without a Cover Charge

1. What were the monthly expenses for your teen center that you established in Unit 4? Divide that amount by the number of days your teen center will be open per month (use a maximum of 30 days per month). This is the **cost per evening** for your teen center.

2. Using your menu, decide what your most popular food item(s) and beverage might be (for example, hamburger, french fries, and soda). Add the prices of these items. Use this total amount as an estimate of your revenue per customer per evening.

Making a Profit for Your Teen Center

3. Make a table like the one below that shows the number of customers and the expected revenue from selling food and drink items and the estimated cost of those items.

Number of customers	Revenue	Cost per evening	Net profit or loss
50	$300	$1,000	-$700
100	$450	$1,000	-$550

4. Using two different colors, draw a **cost** graph and a **revenue** graph on the same set of axes.

5. What is your **cost** equation? What is your **revenue** equation?

6. How many customers will have to enter your center and buy food for you to reach your break-even point?

7. The amount of money beyond your break-even point is your net profit. The amount of money below your break-even point is your net loss. Describe some situations in which your teen center might be in trouble financially. Describe some situations in which your teen center would be very healthy and making a profit. (**Note:** For both parts of this question, a table might be useful.)

8. What would your *ideal* profit be per evening?

9. To make that ideal profit, your teen center would have to sell x amount of servings to your customers. Is your inventory large enough each night to handle the business you would like to have? Based on the food and drink inventory you did in Unit 4, demonstrate, in detail, how your group can meet the needs to make your ideal profit every evening of the month.

10. Did you encounter any problems, such as not enough food and drink for your customers? If you did, would that affect your graphs above? For example, if you do not have enough food and drink, you would need to purchase more and that would affect your overall profit.

11. The above price structure is based on one serving per customer. What is your maximum capacity? Is your number of servings under or over your maximum capacity? If your number of servings is over your maximum capacity, how would you solve this problem?

12. If your group has encountered any problems in getting to the break-even point or making a profit, describe some possible solutions that your teen center could use to overcome these obstacles.

Making a Profit for Your Teen Center

Part II: Price Structure with a Cover Charge

1. Before you can enter some establishments, you have to pay a cover charge. How does your teen center feel about making the customers pay a cover charge? Discuss the advantages and disadvantages of a cover charge. If you had to have a cover charge, what do you feel a fair cover charge would be?

2. Develop a **new revenue chart** that includes the cover charge your teen center decides on. You are still including the most popular food items.

Number of customers	Revenue from from selling food and drink items	Cover charge	Total revenue (food, drink, and cover charge)

3. Draw a **cost** graph and your new **revenue** graph on the same set of axes. Use a red pen for **cost** and a black pen for **revenue**.

4. What is your **cost** equation? Did it change from Part I? What is your new **revenue** equation?

5. Now where is your break-even point?

6. Does your teen center see any advantages to having a cover charge?

7. Again, develop a **net loss and profit chart** that includes the cover charge.

8. Do you think it would be easier to reach your *ideal* profit now?

9. Would the cover charge help you at all if you were short on your inventory? Explain.

10. In conclusion, would your teen center have a cover charge or not have a cover charge? Explain, in detail, why or why not.

A Graphic Investigation

Given the following information, answer the questions below.

A. Teen Center #1 charges $3 for one food item and soft drink and has a $3 cover charge.

B. Teen Center #2 charges $2 for a bag of potato chips and soft drink and has a $6 cover charge.

C. Teen Center #3 charges $3 for just a soft drink but does not have a cover charge.

1. Construct three different tables representing the three different teen centers.

2. Using your own graph paper, draw the graphs of the three different teen centers on the same axes using a different color for each teen center.

3. Write equations for Teen Center #1, Teen Center #2, and Teen Center #3.

4. What would be the y-intercept for Teen Center #1? Teen Center #2? Teen Center #3?

5. What are the real-world meanings for each of the slopes for the three teen centers?

6. What are the real-world meanings for each of the y-intercepts for the three teen centers?

7. When is the cost of going to Teen Center #1 going to equal the cost of going to Teen Center #2?

8. When is the cost of going to Teen Center #2 going to equal the cost of going to Teen Center #3?

9. When is the cost of going to Teen Center #1 going to equal the cost of going to Teen Center #3?

Building the Physical Model

The most fun part of the project was building the physical model. I didn't think we could really turn some pieces of foam board into an actual building. After it was all done I was very surprised and happy. It made me feel good to be part of the group that made such a wonderful looking club.

—Darlene, Deerfield Beach High School, 1995

Building the physical model will provide your students with an opportunity to be creative and to transform their two-dimensional blueprint into a three-dimensional model. This part of the project can be integrated throughout the year with special days set aside for working on the physical model, or it can be completed all at once. The only prerequisite for this unit is that students need to have a complete blueprint (Unit 2) and the room design (Unit 3). It was incredible to see my students at work. They were not doing just what was required, but were also focusing on details and accuracy. For example, they built ramps for people with disabilities, made doors that opened and closed, and even created a sunken dance floor. If nothing else, I have learned that when one has a purpose, working is no longer a problem. Students, as well as anyone, have self-discipline when they have a reason to be engaged.

Mathematical Concepts

- Measurement
- Area and perimeter
- Ratio and proportion
- Scale drawings

Lesson

- 6-1: Building the Model

Assessment

I did not grade the physical models. I had my pre-calculus class and other mathematics teachers grade the models for accuracy, and then I had other classes and teachers judge them for creativity. I have included a specific grade sheet you may want people to use. When I gave such a grade sheet to the group of students, it included all the comments that all the judges had made.

Extension

Since I had no knowledge about how to build a physical model, I invited our school's drama teacher, whose expertise is set design, to share his knowledge with my classes. He told them what supplies they would need (for example, foam board or illustration board, an X-acto® knife, and glue), where to buy the materials, what tools were needed (for example, T-squares, paint, protractors, compasses, templates, drawing triangles), and he demonstrated the building of a physical model. Through his presentation, students observed the use of mathematics outside the traditional classroom. I suggest taking photos of their final products which they can use in their reports.

I suggest working with your art, drama, or industrial arts teachers, for they will be invaluable at this point. This part of the project was the most exciting for my students—they finally had an opportunity to bring mathematics to life.

Teen Center Name _____

Names _____

Building the Physical Model

(40 points)   Accuracy _____ Comments _____

_____

_____

(40 points)   Feasibility _____ Comments _____

_____

_____

(20 points)   Neatness _____ Comments _____

_____

_____

TOTAL POINTS _____

It will take the students at least five to six hours to build their physical model. I suggest that they build the model in class, because it would be cumbersome for them to carry the project to and from home. It is the most exciting part of the project and it was well worth my time and my students' time.

Here are some suggestions from my students on how to build a physical model:

- Build everything necessary in the rooms before putting up the walls.
- Certain types of paint (tempera) warp the physical model.
- Using foil for walls will add a mirror effect.
- Use colored foam board or illustration board.
- Paint or wallpaper walls before gluing them to foam board.

Objective

- To provide students with the opportunity to apply mathematics in building a physical model

Materials

The amount spent on materials will depend on donations from various stores in your area. The expenses for the materials my students used were minimal because of all the donations we received.

- Foam board
- Illustration board
- X-acto knives
- Cardboard
- Templates with circles, squares, rectangles, parallelograms, and triangles
- Templates for bathroom, kitchen, living room, and dining room
- Glue
- T-square
- Drawing triangle
- Paint
- Straight pins with and without little circular knobs
- Popsicle sticks
- Foil
- Push pins
- Paper fasteners
- Wallpaper sample books
- Sample carpeting

Resource

• Group Activity 6-1: Instructions for Building the Model

Class Activity 6-1
Demonstration   50 minutes

I suggest that you invite someone to your class who can teach or show your students how to construct the physical model. Without Peter Denike, our school's drama teacher, I could never have taught my students how to make a physical model. Prior to starting this part of the project, I invited him to our class to demonstrate how to build a physical model. Since his expertise is set design, he brought along one of his models so that students could see what a finished product looks like. He showed them how to do the following:

• Use foam board as their base and to glue the blueprint right to the board
• Set up their rooms first
• Use a T-square to form perfect right angles
• Use an X-acto knife to score their foam board and illustration board
• Cut a "V" on the tip of the glue bottle so that the glue would not run all over
• Glue their walls and other objects
• Make doors that opened and closed
• Use the round part of a straight pin for a door knob
• Make removable walls
• Construct a male and a female figure to scale so that when you looked in the door of the model, it looked realistic

Group Activity 6-1
Instructions for Building the Model   180 minutes

I have included some very basic instructions on how to build the physical model. After that, it is up to the students. This is the activity where their creativity comes alive. One important issue I noticed with my classes was that in their excitement, students sometimes lost their focus and did not always keep the three-dimensional items they were building to scale. Also, it is important to keep them working at a pace that will allow them to meet their time line.

Instructions for Building the Model

It is now time for your group to build your physical model. Below are some basic instructions that your group needs to follow. You may build or create anything you like, but you will not lose any credit if you leave certain items, such as furniture and games, two dimensional. Remember, if you do make something three-dimensional, keep it to scale. Also, a little glue goes a long way, and make sure you cut a "V" on the tip of the glue bottle so that the glue does not ooze out all over the place.

Your physical model will be graded for accuracy, creativity, and neatness.

Instructions

- Glue your blueprint to the foam board, the thicker of the two types of boards.

- If you need to cut your foam board, remember to "score" it and be patient. Also, place cardboard underneath the area you are cutting so that you do not cut into the table, desk, or floor.

Instructions for Building the Model

- Lay out each of your rooms by using the room layouts from Unit 3. Glue down your flooring and then build everything you want to be three-dimensional. Remember to keep these items to scale. Be sure to glue everything down before putting up the walls.

- Cut your walls using the illustration board, the thinner of the two boards. Make your walls 12 feet high. Again, be patient when "scoring," and use the T-square so that your cuts are at 90-degree angles. You will have much better fits when gluing.

- Cut your windows and doors out of the wall areas. Paint or put on wallpaper before gluing walls to each other and to the blueprint. Work inside out and be patient with the gluing process. Hold at least three or four minutes.

- Finally, out of cardboard build scale figures representing at least two members of your group and place them in your teen center. If you look through the doors, everything should look in proper scale.

Good luck and have fun!

Unit 7
The Business Loan

*Ms. Grigg went over a checklist for making the loan: our business
plan, our checklist for business credit, and our prospect checklist.
She explained each item on every sheet and gave us examples of the
ones we didn't understand. We learned that the bank requires a lot of
information about each individual's financial background. We also
learned that the bank goes to the property for an appraisal to see if
we are paying too much or too little. The visit to the bank isn't a
scary one or a boring one either but an educational one. As you can
see, Bank Atlantic gave us a "void" check for $400,000.*

—Heather, Deerfield Beach High School, 1995

By this time, students should
understand that when working with
linear functions, an additive change that
is constant always results in a straight
line. However, in the world of banking,
students are exposed to exponential
growth (multiplicative change), which
is a very important concept for them to
understand as future consumers. Before
exploring the world of banking and its
complicated formulas, my students did
some exploration of exponents and
developed explicit formulas. Symbolic
representation of exponential functions
is a necessity as the numbers get larger and larger.

Some of this unit's problems come from a source that is a working draft
by the NCTM, called *A Framework Constructing a Vision of Algebra,*
published in September 1994. The students will be asked to recognize
patterns, create tables and graphs, and then develop formulas. The graphing
calculator will be incorporated throughout the unit.

Before each group does the business loan for their teen center, the concept of exponential growth is introduced. Through the study of both linear and exponential patterns, students have the opportunity to recognize the differences between the two types of patterns and to tell how the variables appear differently. Students will see in exponential functions that there is a constant base and a variable exponent. They will be exposed to application problems that include working with savings accounts, car loans, and mortgages.

Mathematical Concepts

- Exponential growth
- Recursive and explicit formulas
- Properties of exponents
- Distributive property
- Domain and range

Lessons

- 7-1: Paper-Folding Problem
- 7-2: Allowance Problem
- 7-3: Savings Account Problem
- 7-4: Home Mortgage Problem
- 7-5: Teen Center Business Loan

Assessment

Individual Activity 7-2: The Allowance Problem could be used as a quiz because it assesses each student's understanding of exponential equations. It also reviews linear equations. The day after students do Home Activity 7-3: The Car Depreciation Problem, they could do an investigation of various different cars they are interested in.

Also, after doing Individual Activity 7-4: The Home Mortgage Problem, students could investigate their own dream home at the present rate of interest.

The Business Loan Report is a key report for each teen center group and should be a major grade for their teen center project. The group's thoroughness and their use of exponential functions should be considered when the report is graded.

I was introduced to this problem at a workshop and found it to be a wonderful way to introduce exponential functions to students. Some students will explore the problem at a simple level at first and try to find ways to add; others will double. But some will realize that the solution is an exponential function with a power of 2. By requiring the students to make a table as they are folding and graphing, the need for an equation arises. The opportunity for discussion presents itself when students realize that they are dealing with repeated multiplication and when they understand that the definition of multiplication is repeated addition and that exponentiation is repeated multiplication.

The graphing calculator is useful to show the recursive pattern. Students will realize that recursion has its limitations and that an explicit formula is useful because it allows them to solve for any variable.

Objective

- To help students develop the ability to recognize the pattern, then develop an equation for an increasing or decreasing exponential function

Materials

- One $8\frac{1}{2}$-by-11-inch piece of paper for each student
- Graphing calculator

Resources

- Class Activity 7-1: Paper-Folding
- Home Activity 7-1: Exploring Exponential Decay

 ### Class Activity 7-1
Paper-Folding   60 minutes

I suggest that you have students sit in groups and do the exploring, and as each part of the exploration concludes, there can be class discussion. In this way, the activity becomes a teacher-guided exploration of exponential growth. With a few simple folds of the paper a very powerful concept is introduced.

Working with the folded piece of paper, students can explore the area of the regions as they fold the paper into progressively smaller areas. This is an excellent way to introduce negative exponents, but should probably be discussed the following day. It is interesting to note if students understand that the area is decreasing by a decay factor of $\frac{1}{2}$ and are able to develop the equation $y = \frac{1}{2}x^2$.

Paper-Folding

Take a sheet of paper and fold it in half as shown.

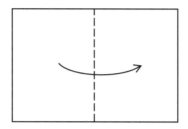

Your first fold divided the paper into two regions.

Rotate the paper 90 degrees and fold it in half again. You have now divided the paper into four regions.

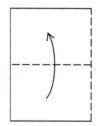

1. Continue folding the paper in half until you have done it at least seven times. After each fold, calculate or count the number of regions. Make a table like the one below to record your results.

Number of folds	Number of regions
0	1
1	2
2	4

2. As you went from one fold to the next, how did the number of regions increase?

3. Did the number of regions increase by the same number each time?

4. Start with the number 2 and use your calculator to keep doubling it. The first four numbers you should get are 2, 4, 8, 16. On most calculators, to do this you push 2; enter; × 2 enter; then push enter repeatedly to keep doubling. Do the numbers you get look familiar?

5. Suppose your paper was thin enough to make as many folds as you wanted to. How many folds would you have to make to get at least 1000 regions? How many to make at least 1,000,000 regions?

6. Write an equation for the number of regions (y) based on the number of folds x.

Exploring Exponential Decay

Using the paper you folded today in class, investigate the following:

1. As you increase the number of folds, what is happening to the area of each region? Make a table as you did in the class activity today, but replace **Number of regions** with **Area of region**.

2. If you could continue to fold the paper in half forever, would the area of each region ever reach 0?

3. Write an equation that shows the area of each region per number of folds.

4. What happens to the number of regions and the area of the regions if you fold the paper by thirds?

In this lesson, students compare the growth differences between a linear function and an exponential function. It is important to review the home activity from Lesson 7-1 because it provides an opportunity to introduce negative exponents. Because properties of exponents have not been formally introduced, extra time might be used in the class activity to formally introduce them.

Objective

- To help students develop the ability to recognize the differences between an exponential function and a linear function

Materials

- Graphing calculator

Resources

- Transparency 7-2: Exponential Growth vs. Exponential Decay
- Individual Activity 7-2: The Allowance Problem
- Home Activity 7-2: The Stacking Pennies Problem

 Class Activity 7-2
Review of Home Activity 7-1   30 minutes

Reviewing the home activity is important because it helps students realize that the base is a fraction of $\frac{1}{2}$ and that the equation is $y = \left(\frac{1}{2}\right)^x$. At this time, introduce the general form of the exponential equation, $y = ab^x$ and do the following:

- Discuss negative exponents.
- Show that for $b > 1$ the rate of growth increases.
- Show that for $b < 1$ the pattern is an exponential decay and the decay factor of b.

Transparency 7-2 shows exponential growth of $y = 2^x$ and exponential decay of $y = 2^{-x}$.

Individual Activity 7-2
The Allowance Problem   45 minutes

The purpose of this activity is for students to use tables and graphs, to recognize patterns, and then to develop equations for two different functions—one linear and the other exponential. A discussion can follow that shows that the linear function has an additive change while the exponential function has a multiplicative change.

Home Activity 7-2
The Stacking Pennies Problem

This problem is similar to the allowance problem and reinforces the differences between a linear function and an exponential function.

Exponential Growth vs. Exponential Decay

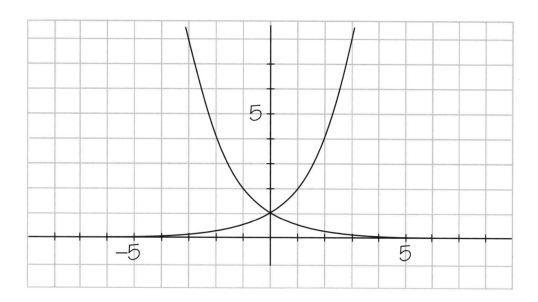

$$y = 2^x \text{ and } y = \left(\tfrac{1}{2}\right)^x = 2^{-x}$$

The Allowance Problem

Pablo and Maria are given the choice between two different allowances. Pablo chooses Plan A and Maria chooses Plan B. Who has made the better deal?

Plan A: An allowance of $10 to start plus $2 each succeeding week. For the first week, the allowance is $12; for the second week it is $14; for the third week, $16; and so on.

Plan B: An allowance of 1¢ to start and then 2¢ for the first week, 4¢ for the second week, 8¢ for the third week, and so on.

To represent which of the plans is better, do the following:

1. Make a table up to 12 weeks that shows both plans. Make sure you start with Week 0, when Pablo is paid his initial $10 and Maria is paid her initial 1¢.
2. Graph both plans.
3. Write equations for each plan. Make sure they are correct. How do you know if your equations are correct?
4. What types of equations do you have?
5. Which is the better plan and why?

The Stacking Pennies Problem

Suppose we stack pennies in the following manner:

Stack	1	2	3	4	5	6
Plan 1	2	4	6	8		
Plan 2	1	2	4	8		

Which plan will give you the most money? Prove your argument with the use of tables, graphs, and equations.

Savings Account Problem

In this lesson, students examine the exponential growth of money in savings accounts and then study car-depreciation problems. All of the problems continually refer back to the paper-folding problem. Again, depending on where you teach, many of your students might not currently have savings accounts or cars. However, these are realistic situations that students may wish to investigate some day. This lesson also provides a transition to the mortgage and bank loan activities in Lesson 7-5.

Objective
- To help students recognize that the amount of money in a savings account grows in an exponential pattern, and to write equations applicable to similar situations involving mortgages and interest

Materials
- Graphing calculator

Resources
- Group Activity 7-3: The Savings Account Problem
- Home Activity 7-3: The Car Depreciation Problem

Class Activity 7-3
Review of Home Activity 7-2   15 minutes

To review Home Activity 7-2, have students work in groups and compare their answers. Each group should decide on a quality response. Choose one of the groups to present their reasoning orally. Then have a class discussion on any other methods individuals or groups pursued. I usually collect this assignment even after it is reviewed in class to give me an idea of their understanding of the assignment.

Group Activity 7-3
The Savings Account Problem   40 minutes

Students should understand how money will grow in a savings account after a number of years. My students have no trouble seeing that growth is exponential, but they have problems with what to do with the interest. They forget to take 1 and then add the rate. They want to deal only with the rate, not 1 + the rate. The other problem they have is converting 5% to a decimal; some will use 0.5 instead of 0.05. My students are able to figure out the pattern fairly quickly, but they need some time with the development of the equation.

Home Activity 7-3
The Car Depreciation Problem

This problem has students work with exponential decay (describes growth in reverse). The setup is very similar to that of the savings account problem, except that the students must subtract the rate from 1. Numerous problems are available for exponential decay with radioactivity, but I have chosen the example of a car because most students can relate to owning or wanting to own a car.

The Savings Account Problem

1. If Pablo invested $1,000 at 6% interest compounded annually and no money was withdrawn, how much money would he have after 5 years; 8 years; 50 years; *n* years?

2. Make a chart showing 1 to 10 years and remember that at the first year Pablo's initial investment was $1,000.

3. Create a graph.

4. Write an exponential equation. Describe which variable represents years and which variable represents the total amount of money.

The Car Depreciation Problem

1. Most automobiles depreciate in value every year. Suppose that a brand-new automobile costs $20,000 and loses one-fifth of its value every year. What is the value of this car after 2 years; 7 years; n years? When will the value of the car be half of the original value? Will the car ever be worth absolutely nothing?

2. Make a chart showing the value of the car for the first 10 years and remember the initial value (year 0) of the car, $20,000.

3. Create a graph.

4. Write an exponential equation. Describe which variable represents years and which variable represents the total amount of money.

This lesson gives the students an opportunity to work with some pretty complicated formulas, but with the help of the graphing calculator they are more manageable. The most dramatic aspect of this lesson for my students was that banks make a lot of interest on the money they loan to people. This really got the students' attention!

Objective
- To help students use and work with complicated mortgage formulas

Materials
- Graphing calculator

Resources
- Individual Activity 7-4: The Home Mortgage Problem
- Home Activity 7-4: Big Al's Dilemma

Class Activity 7-4
Review of Home Activity 7-3   15 minutes

Again, the home activity emphasizes exponential decay versus exponential growth. Also, since students have not done logarithms, the graphing calculator's TRACE function is invaluable in finding the half life.
The differences between growth of $y = 1000(1 + 0.06)^x$ as in Group Activity 7-3: The Savings Account Problem, the equation for the car is $y = 20,000(1 - 0.2)^x$ showing exponential decay.

Individual Activity 7-4
The Home Mortgage Problem   45 minutes

Though this is an individual activity, students may work on it in their groups so that they can talk to each other if they are having problems. As an individual activity versus a group activity, each student should do the entire exercise. Because the formulas are complicated, I believe students need to punch the buttons to get the feeling of what is going on.

Home Activity 7-4
Big Al's Dilemma

This writing exercise has the students compare the features of a linear function with those of an exponential function. It can be used as a form of assessment and collected the day after it's completed.

The Home Mortgage Problem

An $80,000 home mortgage for 35 years at 9.5% has a monthly payment of $657. Part of the monthly payment goes for the interest charge on the unpaid balance and the remainder of the payment is used to reduce the principal. The amount that goes for interest is given by the formula

$$u = M - \left(M - \frac{Pr}{12}\right)\left(1 + \frac{r}{12}\right)^{12t}$$

The amount that goes toward reduction of the principal is given by

$$v = \left(M - \frac{Pr}{12}\right)\left(1 + \frac{r}{12}\right)^{12t}$$

In these formulas, P is the amount of the mortgage, r is the interest rate, M is the monthly payment, and t is the time in years.

1. Use your graphing calculator to graph each function in the same window and show the 35 years of mortgage payments. (**Note:** When you are doing this problem, replace all the variables with the information given, except for time.)

   To put this in the calculator, enter the equations the following way. Remember the u and the v will be y_1 and y_2. For t you will use x. For example, if your calculator is a TI-83, your screens will look like this:

Enter functions	Set window	See graph

   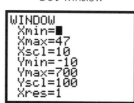 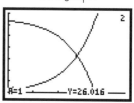

   Using your TRACE button, you can find out at year 1 (x-value) on the top graph that the financial institution is receiving about $630.98 in interest a month. The bottom graph shows that out of the $657.00 monthly payment, you are paying only $26.02 toward the principal ($80,000).

The Home Mortgage Problem

a. Once you have set your windows and graphed to two functions, make a table like the one below for the 35 years of the loan.

Year	Principal	Interest
2	29.52	
5		$618.27
10		
15		
20		
25		
30		
35		

b. In the early years of the mortgage, the larger part of the monthly payment goes for what purpose?

2. Approximate the time when the monthly payment is evenly divided between interest and principal reduction.

3. The total interest paid on a home mortgage of P dollars, at interest rate r for t years, is given by the formula

$$u = P \left[\frac{rt}{1 - \left(\frac{1}{1 + \frac{r}{12}} \right)^{12t}} - 1 \right]$$

a. How much interest is the bank receiving on this $80,000 home mortgage at 9.5%?

Use a graphing calculator to graph the total interest function. If you are using a TI-83, your screens will look like this:

Enter functions   Set window   Trace graph

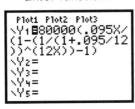

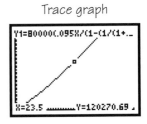

The graph shows how much interest you have paid after a number of years.

The Home Mortgage Problem

b. Make a table like the one below using your TRACE button.

Number of years	Total amount of interest paid
1	$4,176.17
5	
10	
15	
20	
25	
30	
35	

4. Do not get confused with monthly payments and how much you are paying per year or years. In a year, you would be making 12 payments. How many total payments would you make in 35 years?

5. Were you surprised at how much interest would be paid over the 35-year period of the loan? Explain.

6. Describe the differences you have noted between linear functions and exponential functions. Why do you think financial institutions have chosen exponential functions, rather than linear functions, for the interest they charge on loans? Give an example that demonstrates the difference between linear functions and exponential functions using the $80,000 home mortgage.

Big Al's Dilemma

Big Al is the noted math expert in the village of Mathemania. To the townspeople he knows all—however, this is just a big bluff. He surrounds himself with advisors who are the wisest and the best in the world. Big Al has put out a want ad in your town's newspaper because he is looking for a tax advisor who will help Mathemania with its very large financial problems.

When you apply for the job, you find out that Big Al's other advisors have told him that if each of the townspeople is initially charged $100 and then $20 a month thereafter, it will help solve Mathemania's financial problems for the upcoming year. However, you feel that if each person is initially charged $100 and then charged 20% interest on the $100 compounded monthly, Mathemania will be in even better shape at the end of the year.

Big Al needs to have everything proved in great detail, so you are going to sit down and make up tables, graphs, and equations to prove that your method will provide much more money for Mathemania than Big Al's other advisors' method.

Teen Center Business Loan

When I originally piloted the project, I sent each group to the bank to meet with a loan officer. If you can get your class to the bank, this is an incredible experience. (I had students who had never even seen the inside of a bank.) However, if you cannot do this, then try to have a loan officer come in and speak to the class. I've found that loan officers are more than willing to offer their expertise. The loan officers who visited my classes brought in loan applications, and when my students went to the various banks, they received "voided" checks for the amounts they needed to "borrow." When the loan officer came to class, I had my students lay out their physical model along with their projected expenses and their projected profit. The community members in general were extremely impressed and always asked me why they never had a chance to do this when they were in school.

At some points in their lives, your students will need to borrow money. With the exponential lessons they have just done, they have a pretty good idea that it costs a lot of money to borrow money.

 **Group Activity 7-5**
The Business Loan Report   75 minutes

Before the loan officer comes to class, each group needs to familiarize themselves with certain banking terms. Have students prepare some questions to ask the loan officer. They should write a report after the loan officer has talked to the class.

 **Class Activity 7-5**
Visit By Loan Officer   60 minutes

This activity works best if your class period is an hour and a half. This is where block scheduling is invaluable because the loan officer can spend a few minutes *with each group* looking at the individual projects; talking about the process of taking out a loan; and then fielding some questions. Each group should have three questions prepared to ask the loan officer. The questions should be prioritized according to their importance, in case the loan officer can take only one or two questions from each group.

The Business Loan Report

With the upcoming visit from the loan officer, you need to retrieve certain parts of your previous reports and find the following:

The amount you plan to borrow from the bank _____

Your monthly payment _____

The number of years you will be repaying the loan _____

The amount of the repayment that will be interest _____

What do you feel could be your nightly profit? _____

Monthly profit? _____ Yearly profit? _____

To help you develop a banking vocabulary, find the definitions for the following terms:

Loan	Collateral
Principal	Down payment
Mortgage	Amortization chart
Interest	Balloon payment

Develop three questions that your group would like to ask the loan officer about getting a business loan of this magnitude.

After the loan officer visits your classroom, each of you will write a report about the loan officer's visit and how it affected you. In your report, include at least three different aspects of loans that you learned from the loan officer.

When we started this project it was going to be an easy A but it ended up being a way to learn and work together. I learned that for a business to work everyone needs to work together. It takes more than money and a dream to even start out in this world. I learned that math is not just another subject in school but that everything has math in it.

—Amanda, Deerfield Beach High School, 1995

The final part of the teen center project is an individual activity. As a culmination to the project, each student will analyze the project and describe their role (leader or follower) and satisfaction with their own and their team members' performance in the group. The students will also summarize the mathematics they learned, what aspect of the project they enjoyed the most and why, and the biggest problem their group encountered and how they solved it.

	A	B	C	D
23	ROOM 2	150.0	CARPET	8
24	HALL 1	75.0	LINO	WH
25	HALL 2	90.0	LINO	WHI
26	STAIR 1	102.0		BIG
27	BATHRM	60.0	TILE	
28				
29				
30				
31				
32				

Analysis of Teen Center Project

On a separate sheet of paper, answer the questions below. Use complete sentences and paragraphs.

1. Describe your role (recorder, statistician, engineer, or project leader) in your teen center project.

2. What do you feel your greatest contribution(s) were in the completion of the project?

3. List **three** mathematical concepts that you learned while doing the project. Then describe them in detail.

4. Were you satisfied or dissatisfied with your own performance as you were doing the project? Explain.

5. What was the major problem that your group encountered, and how did you all go about solving it?

6. If you had an opportunity to redo the project, what are some of the changes that you would make?

Analysis of Teen Center Project

7. What aspect did you enjoy the most while doing the project, and why?

8. Suppose that you were the project manager and had to make a report to your boss. Provide a brief description of what your team did to successfully complete the project and how you felt you all worked as a team. Imagine you have had some trouble in the past with some of the employees not doing their part, and your boss has told you that if some do not pull their weight, they will have to be let go. Can you defend all of your employees and tell your boss that they should keep their job? Why or why not?

9. Do you have any additional comments about the teen center project?

Answers to Selected Exercises

Individual Activity 2-1

Note: Figures are not drawn to scale. Check student work.

1-3. Answers will vary.

4. Check students' circles.

5. 2π in

6. π in^2

7. a.

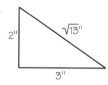

   b. $P = 5 + \sqrt{13}$ in

   c. $A = 3$ in^2

8. Answers will vary

9. $4\frac{3}{4}$ in.

10.

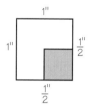

11.

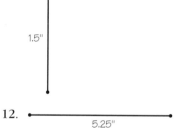

1.5"

12.

5.25"

Home Activity 2-1

1. $12' \times 5'$

2. $10 \text{ m} \times 6 \text{ m}$

3. a. 400 ft^2

   b-c. Answers will vary. Students should note that rectangles that have the same area do not necessarily have the same perimeter.

4. 26 ft^2

5. a. 444 ft^2

   b. $1{,}332$ ft^2

Transparency 2-3

Area (A) = 100 ft^2
Area (B) = 80 ft^2
Area (C) = 50π ft^2 or 157.0 ft^2
Area (D) = $390 - 50\pi$ ft^2 or 232.9 ft^2
Area (E) = 39 ft^2
Area (F) = 171 ft^2
Total Area (by adding) = 779.9 ft^2
Total area = 780 ft^2

Individual Activity 2-3

1. 8 ft

2.

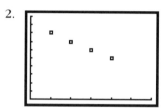

3. $w = 1.5$ ft

4. a. Perimeter I = $13 \text{ ft} \times 18 \text{ ft}$
      Perimeter II = $45 \text{ ft} \times 24 \text{ ft}$
      Perimeter III = $20 \text{ ft} \times 10 \text{ ft}$
   b. Total area = $1{,}514$ ft^2

5. $A = 27{,}500$ ft^2

6. A right triangle. $P = 12$ units; $A = 6$ units^2

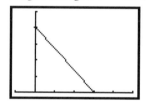

7. a. $A = 49.2$ ft^2
   b. $P = 41.14$ ft

Transparency 2-4

1. $9{:}25$

2. a. $34{:}30 = 17{:}15$
   b. $2{:}1$

Home Activity 2-4

1. $9{:}25$

2. a. $14{:}12 = 7{:}6$
   b. $2{:}1$

3. $15 \text{ ft} \times 7.5 \text{ ft}$

4. 12.5 yd^2

5. $\$178.63$

Home Activity 3-1

1.

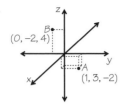

$(0, -2, 4)$ B
$(1, 3, -2)$ A

2. a. Check graph
   b. 120 units^3
   c. 148 units^2

3. a.

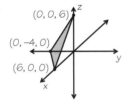

$(0, 0, 6)$
$(0, -4, 0)$
$(6, 0, 0)$

   b.

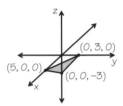

$(0, 3, 0)$
$(5, 0, 0)$
$(0, 0, -3)$

Home Activity 3-2

1. Price of the paint for the room is $59.10

2-5. Answers will vary.

6. a. Check students work.
   b. Graphs are parallel.

Home Activity 3-3

1. $A = x(60 - 2x)$

2.

$60 - 2x$
x x

3.

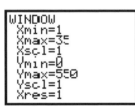

```
WINDOW
 Xmin=1
 Xmax=35
 Xscl=1
 Ymin=0
 Ymax=550
 Yscl=1
 Xres=1
```

4.

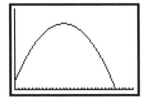

5.

30'
15'   15'

Area is maximized when
$x \approx 15$ ft. Max. area $= 450$ ft^2.

Group Activity 3-4

Inventory After Restock

Brand	Large	Medium	Small
MacWard	44	32	20
Sparky's	47	53	31
Laritz	50	42	27
Baydines	80	57	80

Inventory After Sales

Brand	Large	Medium	Small
MacWard	29	20	13
Sparky's	9	29	18
Laritz	44	25	19
Baydines	62	17	61

Retail Prices

Brand	Large	Medium	Small
MacWard	$64.38	$51.88	$39.38
Sparky's	$72.38	$59.88	$47.38
Laritz	$82.00	$64.50	$54.50
Baydines	$100.00	$87.50	$75.00

Home Activity 3-4

1. The scalar multiplier is 1.15. This is the resulting matrix.

$$\begin{bmatrix} \$52,900 & \$26,450 & \$21,850 \\ \$56,350 & \$28,750 & \$24,150 \\ \$60,950 & \$33,350 & \$27,600 \end{bmatrix}$$

2. $$\begin{bmatrix} 2 & -2 & -3 \\ -3 & 12 & -8 \\ 3 & 5 & -1 \end{bmatrix}$$

3. $$\begin{bmatrix} -10 & 6 & 1 \\ 15 & -2 & 2 \\ -1 & 11 & 19 \end{bmatrix}$$

4. $$\begin{bmatrix} -2 & 2 & 3 \\ 3 & -12 & 8 \\ -3 & -5 & 1 \end{bmatrix}$$

5. $\begin{bmatrix} -8 & 5 & 1.5 \\ 12 & -4.5 & 3.5 \\ -1.5 & 7 & 14.5 \end{bmatrix}$

6. $\begin{bmatrix} -26 & 20 & 18 \\ 39 & -69 & 47 \\ -18 & -11 & 34 \end{bmatrix}$

7. $\begin{bmatrix} -18 & 10 & -1 \\ 27 & 8 & -4 \\ 1 & 27 & 37 \end{bmatrix}$

8. $a = 2; b = 5; c = 4; d = 11;$
   $e = 12; f = 22; g = 9; h = 6;$
   $i = \frac{4}{5}; j = 3; k = 10; l = 11;$
   $m = 8; n = 1; o = 0; p = 19$

Class Activity 3-5

1. 80 strips

2. 55 strips

3. 56 strips

4. 38 strips

5. $\begin{bmatrix} 80 & 55 \\ 56 & 38 \end{bmatrix}$

6. $\begin{bmatrix} ae + bg & af + bh \\ ce + dg & cf + dh \end{bmatrix}$

7. $\begin{bmatrix} \$90.25 \\ \$62.90 \end{bmatrix}$

8. The cost matrix shows cost per strip.

9. $90.25

10. $62.90

11. The expense matrix shows the cost for each person's work.

Group Activity 3-5

Stock Value

MacWard	$890
Sparky's	$2,000
Laritz	$765
Baydines	$1,920

Sales Income

MacWard	$662
Sparky's	$2,069
Laritz	$793
Baydines	$1,756

Store Expenses

MacWard	$370
Sparky's	$1,140
Laritz	$430
Baydines	$975

Profits

MacWard	$292
Sparky's	$929
Laritz	$363
Baydines	$781
Total	$2,365

Home Activity 3-5

1. a. Mother $1,500.48
   Father $2,186.21
   Child 1 $660.64
   Child 2 $1,095.65
   b. Total cost is $5,442.98.
   c. $142.78

2. a. $\begin{bmatrix} -71 & -52 \\ 36 & 62 \end{bmatrix}$

   b. $\begin{bmatrix} 59 & 13 \\ -4 & 42 \end{bmatrix}$

   c. $\begin{bmatrix} -52 & -71 \\ 62 & 36 \end{bmatrix}$

3. Total cost is $7,290.

Room	Total
Dining	$2,600
Game	$3,260
Kitchen	$280
Office	$1,150

Partner Activity 5-1

1. Answers may vary. Students should note that the first number is the x-coordinate and the second is the y-coordinate.

2. a. ii
   b. vii
   c. i
   d. iii
   e. iv
   f. vi
   g. v

3. a. 1; b. -4

4. A straight line

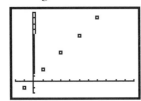

5. They form the parabola $y = x^2$

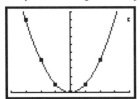

6. $A(2, 1); B(-5, -4); C(-4, 3); D(2, -1)$

Home Activity 5-1

2. Student graph should indicate that they would earn more working at Joline's.

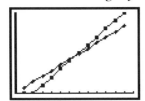

Group Activity 5-2

1.

m	1	2	3	4	5	6
g	3	6	9	12	15	18

2. 21 gallons

3. $G = 3M$

4.

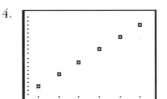

5. 60 gallons

6. Yes. See graph below.

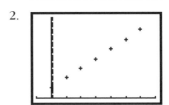

Home Activity 5-2

1.

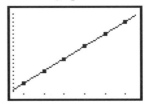

2.

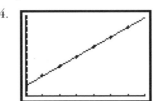

3. $y = 6x + 6.50$

4.

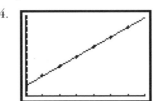

5. Cost of 150 towels = \$906.50
   Cost of 200 towels = \$1,206.50

Group Activity 5-3

2. The number of bags ordered and the total cost.

3. The price per bag and the delivery costs are both constants.

4. \$7.50 for Yvonne's; \$7.00 for Clarence's.

5. The formula tells her the slope of the line between points (x_1, y_1) and (x_2, y_2). Both slopes are constant and represent the cost per bag in each case.

6. She was remembering how to calculate the y-intercept.

7. $y = 7.5x + 10$ for Yvonne's; $y = 7x + 18$ for Clarence's. It would be cheaper to use Clarence's for 50 bags.

8. Yvonne's is cheaper for 15 bags, but Clarence's is cheaper for 20. They charge the same for 16 bags.

Individual Activity 5-3

Part I: Cost

1.
Number	Cost
0	$200
1	203
2	206
3	209
4	212
5	215

2. a. Slope = 3
   b. Cost per T-shirt

3. $y = 3x + 200$

4. The y-intercept is $(0, 200)$. The y-intercept equals the starting costs.

5. Answers will vary.

6. You can use the equation to calculate the costs of producing a given number of T-shirts.

7.
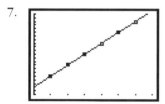

8. Cost for 100 T-shirts = $500
   Cost for 150 T-shirts = $650
   Cost for 450 T-shirts = $1,550

Part II: Revenue

1.
Number	Cost
1	$7.50
2	15.00
3	22.50
4	30.00
5	37.50
6	45.00

2.
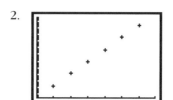

3. The slope is 7.5 and it represents the revenue per T-shirt.

4. The y-intercept is 0 and it represents the revenue from selling no T-shirts.

5. $y = 7.50x$

6.
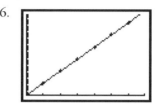

7. Revenue (40) = $300
   Revenue (100) = $750
   Revenue (150) = $1,125
   Revenue (450) = $3,375

8. Check student work. Students should use the TRACE feature and adjust their window to check this.

Part III: Profit

1. The break-even point occurs when your revenue equals your costs.

2.
Number	Cost	Revenue	Net
1	$203	$7.50	−$195.50
5	215	37.50	−177.50
10	230	75.00	−155.00
20	260	150.00	−110.00
30	290	225.00	−65.00
35	305	262.50	−42.50
40	320	300.00	−20.00
45	335	337.50	2.50
50	350	375.00	25.00

3. The break-even point is between 40 and 45 T-shirts sold.

4. The graph shows the break-even point at ≈ 44 T-shirts. But you can't sell a partial T-shirt, so the break-even point is 45 T-shirts.

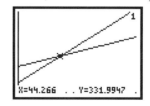

5. $R > \$330$

6. 489 T-shirts

Class Activity 7-1

1.

Folds	Regions
1	2
2	4
3	8
4	16
5	32
6	64
7	128
8	256
9	512

2. It doubled.

3. No, since it was double the previous number it increased by a different amount each time.

4. Answers will vary.

5. You will need at least 10 folds for 1000 regions and 20 folds for a million regions.

6. $y = 2^x$

Home Activity 7-1

1.

Folds	Area of region
1	$\frac{1}{2}$
2	$\frac{1}{4}$
3	$\frac{1}{8}$
4	$\frac{1}{16}$
5	$\frac{1}{32}$
6	$\frac{1}{64}$
7	$\frac{1}{128}$
8	$\frac{1}{256}$
9	$\frac{1}{512}$

2. No. The area will never reach 0, but it will get arbitrarily close to 0. You may want to use this as an opportunity to discuss limits.

3. $y = 1/(2^x)$ or $y = 2^{-x}$

4. The area would decrease by powers of 3.
   $y = 3^{-x}$

Individual Activity 7-2

1.

Week	A	B
0	$10	$0.01
1	12	0.02
2	14	0.04
3	16	0.08
4	18	0.16
5	20	0.32
6	22	0.64
7	24	1.28
8	26	2.56
9	28	5.12
10	30	10.24
11	32	20.48
12	34	40.96

2.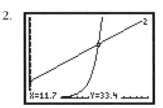

3. Plan A: $y = \$10 + \$2x$
   Plan B: $y = (\$.01)\, 2^x$

4. Plan A is linear. Plan B is exponential.

5. After week 12, Plan B is better. Since Plan B increases exponentially, you will quickly become a millionaire on it.

Home Activity 7-2

Answers will vary. Students should show that Plan 2 is exponential.
Plan 1: $y = 2x$
Plan 2: $y = 2^{x-1}$

Group Activity 7-3

2.

0	$1,000.00
1	1,060.00
2	1,123.60
3	1,191.02
4	1,262.48
5	1,338.23
6	1,418.52
7	1,503.63
8	1,593.85
9	1,689.48
10	1,790.85

3.

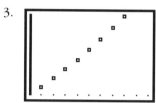

4. $y = 1,000(1.06)^x$

Home Activity 7-3

2.

0	$20,000.00
1	16,000.00
2	12,800.00
3	10,240.00
4	8,192.00
5	6,553.60
6	5,242.88
7	4,194.30
8	3,355.44
9	2,684.35
10	2,147.48

3.

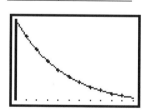

4. $y = 20,000(0.80)^x$

Individual Activity 7-4

1. a.

Year	Principal	Interest
2	$28.60	$628.40
5	37.99	619.01
10	60.97	596.03
15	97.85	559.15
20	157.05	499.95
25	252.07	404.93
30	404.58	252.42
34	590.72	66.28

b. In the early years, most of the payment goes toward the interest.

2. Approximately 28 years

3. a. At $t = 35$ years the bank will receive $276,061.50. That means the total interest on the loan is $196,061.50.

b.

Number of years	Total amount of interest paid
1	$4,176.17
5	20,808.93
10	44,221.66
15	70,368.35
20	98,969.19
25	129,687.20
30	162,166.01
35	196,061.50

4. 420 payments

5. Answers will vary. Students probably will be surprised that the amount of interest paid on the loan is 2.45 times the total loan.

6. Answers will vary.

Appendix: Graphing Calculator Notes for the TI-82 and TI-83

The use of the graphing calculator will greatly enhance many of the activities in this book. The notes below can be used with either the TI-82 or the TI-83. Most of the screen images are from the TI-82, and look slightly different from those on the TI-83. They should cover most of the calculator skills that you will need for the activities in this book. If your students are working with another model, you will need to refer to the guidebook for information on the tasks below.

MODE Settings

Press [MODE] to display a screen like that shown at the right. The settings indicated are the ones that will be used most often in this course. If these settings are not selected, follow the steps below to change the settings.

1. Use the arrow keys to highlight the setting you want to choose.

2. Press [ENTER] to register this selection.

3. When you have the settings you want, press [2nd] [QUIT] to exit from the MODE screen.

Following are explanations of each setting.

First Line—These settings determine the format of the numbers displayed by the calculator. **Normal** is the normal form of the number. It will display as many necessary digits as will fit on a line of the screen (10). **Sci** is the scientific notation form of the number. In scientific notation, the decimal point is positioned so that there is only one digit to its left. The number is multiplied by a power of 10 to compensate for this move. **Eng** is engineering notation. This is similar to scientific notation, except that the powers of 10 are always multiples of 3. You will not use this form in this course.

Second Line—This setting determines the number of decimal places shown. **Float** means that as many places as will fit on the screen will be shown. The number settings are used if you wish to limit the number of decimal places shown. For example, setting this at **2** is useful if you are doing calculations with money.

Third Line—This setting indicates the type of angle measure to be used when doing calculations with trigonometric functions. **Radian** indicates a measuring unit called radian measure, while **Degree** indicates degree measure. In this course you will be using degree mode.

Fourth Line—This setting indicates the form of an equation. **Func** (Function) means that your equations will be entered in the form "$y =$ some expression involving x." **Par** (Parametric) means that you will enter two equations, one for x and one for y, both involving a third variable, t. **Pol** (Polar) means that you enter an equation with r specifying a distance from the center of the graph in terms of an angle. **Seq** (Sequence) means you can graph sequences that are defined recursively or explicitly.

Fifth Line—This setting indicates how the calculator will draw graphs. **Connected** means that it will connect the points as it calculates them. **Dot** means that it will simply plot points on the screen, and not connect them.

Sixth Line—If you have several equations entered, this setting indicates whether they will be graphed **Sequentia**lly or **Simul**taneously.

Seventh Line—FullScreen uses the entire screen for the graph or as the HOME screen. **Split** displays your current graph on the upper half of the screen and uses the lower half of the screen as the HOME screen.

Calculation Keys—Includes a Fraction Function

To perform any arithmetic calculation, enter it, and press ENTER to calculate the answer.

Exponents may be entered in several ways. If you wish to square a number, a variable, or an expression, you can use the x^2 key. This key is located in the left column of keys. To use it, enter the number to be squared, then press x^2 ENTER .

What you enter:

17 x^2 ENTER

What you see:

17^2
                    289

There is also a special key for cubing a number (raising it to the third power). It is not found on any of the regular keys, but must be accessed by using a menu. First type the number or expression that you want to raise to the third power. Press MATH and you will see a screen like that shown at the right. Then

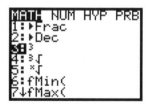

press 3 and an exponent 3 will appear next to your number. (You can also use the arrow keys to position the cursor on choice 3.) Press ENTER to calculate the answer.

You can also use the caret key, ^ , located in the right column of keys, before any number, variable, or expression that you want to enter as an exponent.

What you enter:

2 ^ 5 ENTER

What you see:

2^5
                    32

Be sure to put parentheses around any exponent that involves more than one number. For example, to enter the fractional-exponent expression $3^{2/3}$, press 3 ⟦^⟧ ⟦(⟧ 2 ⟦÷⟧ 3 ⟦)⟧.

Suppose you need to write 0.275 as a fraction. The TI-82 contains a function that will make this conversion directly. Enter .275, and press ⟦MATH⟧ ⟦1⟧ ⟦FRAC⟧ ⟦ENTER⟧, and the calculator will display 11/40.

What you enter:

.275 ⟦MATH⟧ ⟦1⟧ ⟦FRAC⟧ ⟦ENTER⟧

What you see:

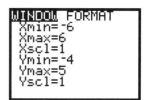

Editing/Replay

The replay, or last entry key (⟦2nd⟧ ⟦ENTRY⟧), reprints previous entries on the screen. Then you can edit what's displayed on the screen by typing over, inserting (⟦2nd⟧ ⟦INS⟧), or deleting (⟦DEL⟧) to change the expression.

The Window Key

Press ⟦WINDOW⟧ to display the current settings for the window variables. For the coordinate axes below, the window values might be those shown on the screen at the right.

Changing the Window Settings

To change one of the values on this screen, use the arrow keys to position the cursor on the value to be changed, and type over the old value. When you finish changing these settings, press ⟦2nd⟧ ⟦QUIT⟧.

Pressing ⟦Y=⟧, or another one of the top-row keys, will allow you to exit from the WINDOW screen.

When setting values for Xmin and Xmax or for Ymin and Ymax, be certain that the minimum value is less than the maximum value.

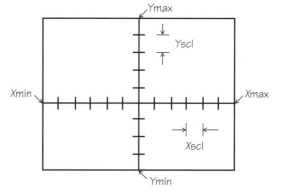

If it isn't, an error message will appear. When choosing settings for Xscl and Yscl, choose values that will place tick marks far enough apart so that they will be easy to distinguish. A value of zero for either scale will place no marks on the respective axis. This is useful when just plotting points. Otherwise, it can be difficult to distinguish the marks on the axis from the plotted points.

The TblSet and TABLE functions allow you to look at the coordinate pairs that will or should be pictured in a graphing window. If you have an equation in $Y=$, you can quickly investigate table values to help determine the correct graphing window.

After pressing 2nd [TBLSET], you can determine the starting x-value (TblMin) and increment for x (∆Tbl) in your table. Press 2nd [TABLE] to see the table for the equation entered.

The TI-82 STAT menu is the best choice for plotting points on the screen because the coordinates are stored in memory as a data set and can be replotted easily. Follow the procedure outlined below.

    i. Clear $Y=$.

    ii. Enter the points as data.

        Type STAT 1 (Edit).

        (If a list needs to be cleared, move the cursor so that the list name is highlighted and press CLEAR ENTER.)

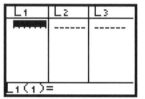

        Enter the x-coordinates in L1 and the y-coordinates in L2.

    iii. Set the plot mode.

        Press 2nd **[STAT PLOT]** 1 (Plot 1 . . .).

        Select On, ⊾∴, L1, L2, ▫.

    iv. Set the graphing window and press GRAPH.

You should see the points on the calculator screen. They can be replotted again when needed in a different graphing window by repeating step iv. Or the entire procedure can be repeated with new coordinates.

If you get a plot error, check to make sure that you have the same number of values in L1 as in L2. In order to stop the calculator from plotting this set of data forever, you will need to turn off the plot in the STAT PLOT menu. (Press 2nd **[STAT PLOT]** 4 (PlotsOff) ENTER.)

Matrices

TI-82

The MATRX EDIT menu allows you to store and use up to five matrices, [A], [B], [C], [D], and [E]. The dimensions are limited to 99 rows or columns or, more likely, by the memory available.

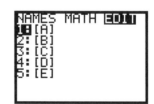

Press MATRX EDIT [1] to edit the dimensions of [A] to the needed size. For this example, be sure the dimensions of [A] are **1 × 2**. Then input the matrix elements.

$$1,1 = \mathbf{20}$$
$$1,2 = \mathbf{220}$$

Press MATRX EDIT [2] to edit matrix [B]. If necessary, change the dimensions of [B] to **2 × 2**. Then input the matrix elements.

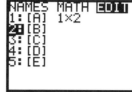
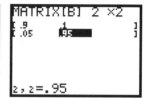

$$1,1 = \mathbf{0.90}$$
$$1,2 = \mathbf{0.10}$$
$$2,1 = \mathbf{0.05}$$
$$2,2 = \mathbf{0.95}$$

When on the HOME screen, enter MATRX [1] ENTER to display the matrix [20   220], and MATRX [2] ENTER to display the matrix

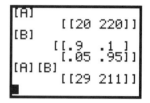

$$\begin{bmatrix} .90 & .10 \\ .05 & .95 \end{bmatrix}$$

Multiply [A] and [B] by pressing MATRX [1] MATRX [2] ENTER.

TI-83

The MATRX EDIT menu allows you to store and use up to ten matrices: [A], [B], [C], [D], [E], [F], [G], [H], [I], and [J]. The dimensions are limited to 99 rows or columns or, more likely, by the memory available.

Press MATRX EDIT [1] to edit the dimensions of [A] to the needed size. For this example, be sure the dimensions of [A] are **1 × 2**. Then input the matrix elements.

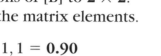

$$1,1 = \mathbf{20}$$
$$1,2 = \mathbf{220}$$

Press MATRX EDIT [2] to edit matrix [B]. If necessary, change the dimensions of [B] to **2 × 2**. Then input the matrix elements.

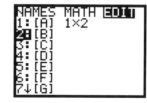

$$1,1 = \mathbf{0.90}$$
$$1,2 = \mathbf{0.10}$$
$$2,1 = \mathbf{0.05}$$
$$2,2 = \mathbf{0.95}$$

When on the HOME screen, enter [MATRX] [1] [ENTER] to display the matrix [20   220], and [MATRX] [2] [ENTER] to display the matrix

$$\begin{bmatrix} .90 & .10 \\ .05 & .95 \end{bmatrix}$$

```
[A]
        [[20 220]]
[B]
        [[.9  .1 ]
         [.05 .95]]
[A][B]
        [[29 211]]
```

Multiply [A] and [B] by pressing [MATRX] [1] [MATRX] [2] [ENTER].

Entering One-Variable Data

TI-82

Six lists of one-variable data can be stored in the TI-82 using the following procedure. Each list can hold up to 99 data values. With this calculator, frequently there are several different methods to accomplish the same result. For example: Enter the list 25, 67, 38, 47, 55, 37, 49, 31, 41, 38 into the calculator. Press [STAT] [1] (Edit . . .). (If a list needs to be cleared, move the cursor so that the list name is highlighted and press [CLEAR] [ENTER].)

```
L1    L2    L3
25    ----- -----
67
38
47
55
L1(6)=
```

Enter the data starting with L1(1). After entering each data value, press [ENTER]. When you're finished entering the data, press [2nd] [QUIT].

TI-83

Lists of one-variable data can be stored in the TI-83 using the following procedure. There are six preset lists in the calculator, and more can be created if needed. There is no specific limit as to the number of entries that can be stored in a list. You are limited to 999 elements per list or, more likely, by the available memory. Frequently there are several different methods that you can use with this calculator to accomplish the same result. For example: Enter the list 25, 67, 38, 47, 55, 37, 49, 31, 41, 38 into the calculator. Press [STAT] [1] (Edit . . .). (If a list needs to be cleared, move the cursor so that the list name is highlighted and press [CLEAR] [ENTER].)

```
L1    L2    L3
25    ----- -----
67
38
47
55
L1(6)=
```

Enter the data starting with L1(1). After entering each data value, press [ENTER]. When you're finished entering the data, press [2nd] [QUIT].